D0832714

The St. Lawrence Seaway

The St. Lawrence Seaway

T. L. HILLS

FREDERICK A. PRAEGER, *Publishers*

NEW YORK

BOOKS THAT MATTER

PUBLISHED IN THE UNITED STATES OF AMERICA
IN 1959
BY FREDERICK A. PRAEGER, INC., PUBLISHERS
64 University Place, New York 3, N. Y.

Second printing, 1960

© T. L. HILLS, 1959

LIBRARY OF CONGRESS CATALOG CARD NUMBER: 59–12718

Contents

Illustrations

PLATES

7

Illustrations

MAPS

ACKNOWLEDGMENTS

Plates 1, 2, 3, 4, 5, 6, 7, 8, 9, 10, 16, – photos: Van der Aa, Montreal, P.Q. Plates 11, 12, 13, 14, 18, 19, 20, – photos: Ontario Hydro. Plate 15, – photo: Office of Information, St. Lawrence Seaway. Plate 17, – photo: Capital Press Service.

Maps 1 and 2 were drawn by W. H. Bromage.

Introduction

In April 1959, as the spring sun over North America warms the land and its rivers, the ice on the mighty St Lawrence River will break up and free this great routeway for the shipping of many nations. On June 26th Her Majesty Queen Elizabeth II, on behalf of Canada, and President Eisenhower, on behalf of the United States, will officially open the St Lawrence Seaway. This opening will bring to completion nearly five years of design and construction of both the Seaway and the Power projects. It will bring to fruition over fifty years of almost incessant agitation in both the United States and Canada for the development of a deep waterway into the heart of the North American continent. Yet the St Lawrence Seaway is just one stage in a process that has been going on for nearly four hundred years, since Jacques Cartier was halted in his journey up the St Lawrence River by the Lachine Rapids. There are many who consider that even the present Seaway is inadequate for present and future needs, and that if the term 'Seaway' is not to become a misnomer, then further enlargement of the channels, canals and locks will be necessary in the not too distant future to bring the St Lawrence Seaway into line with the other great canal systems of the world. At present the Panama, Amsterdam–Rhine, Kiel, Suez, Texas, and Manchester ship canal systems all exceed in size the proportions of the St Lawrence Seaway facilities.

However, the success of the Seaway will not necessarily be judged by the number of overseas ships which may ply the Seaway and the Great Lakes in the future. The Seaway was built primarily to move Quebec-Labrador iron ore from the lower St Lawrence to the Great Lakes in low-cost transportation ore carriers, shallow-draught vessels constructed specially for the trade, and to move grain from the Great

Introduction

Lakes to St Lawrence transhipment ports, thus avoiding one or more transhipments and producing savings in transportation costs by the use of large-capacity, specialised grain carriers. The future of the Seaway for the movement of iron ore and grain appears to be assured. Equally well assured is the success of the Power project. The United States and Canada will share equally the total of 2.2 million h.p. of electricity which will be available by late 1959. Upper New York State and southern Ontario have been hungry for cheap electric power for a long time, so that a market existed long before construction of power facilities started. Regardless of the exact nature of future Seaway traffic, the combined Seaway and Power projects is a magnificent achievement, not only in the field of engineering but also in the field of international co-operation.

This book is a story of the long series of events leading up to the launching of the Seaway and the Power projects, and of their successful completion. It attempts to be neither a complete geography nor a complete history of the development. In the course of five chapters the geographical basis of the Great Lakes–St Lawrence waterway and the development of hydroelectric power is briefly discussed. The discovery and exploration of the Great Lakes–St Lawrence drainage basin is surveyed. The construction and the economic function of the earlier St Lawrence and Great Lakes canal systems are traced from the earliest Lachine Canal to the end of the 14-foot canal era. The idea and the creation of a deep waterway is then discussed, with equal attention being given to the United States and the Canadian points of view. A journey will be taken up the Seaway into the Great Lakes to familiarise readers with the exact nature of the Seaway and Power projects. And finally – what of the future?

In the preparation of this text reference has been made to a number of excellent studies of various aspects of the Great Lakes–St Lawrence deep waterway. For the benefit of those who may wish to read further on this subject and in order to pay acknowledgement for ideas and certain factual material, these publications are recommended: *The St Lawrence Deep Waterway – A Canadian Appraisal* by C. P. Wright (The Macmillan Company of Canada Limited, Toronto, 1935); *The St Lawrence Seaway Manual – a compilation of documents on the Great Lakes Seaway project and correlated Power development* (Document No. 165, U.S. Government Printing Office, Washington,

Introduction

1955); *The Effects of the St Lawrence Seaway on Grain Movements* by Joseph R. Hartley (Bureau of Business Research, School of Business, Indiana University, Bloomington, Indiana, 1957); *The Impact of the St Lawrence Seaway on the Montreal Area* (Montreal Research Council, School of Commerce, McGill University, Montreal, Canada, 1958); *The Lachine Canal* by E. Allan Cureton (unpublished M.A. thesis, McGill University, Montreal, 1957); *The Engineering Journal* and *The Canadian Mining and Metallurgical Bulletin* (various articles published between 1955 and 1958, especially 'Planning and Constructing the Lachine Section' by L. H. Burpee, *E.J.*, September 1958).

Finally, I wish to pay acknowledgement to the assistance readily offered by Mr John Akin, Information Officer, St Lawrence Seaway Authority, Ottawa. Over a four-year period he has kept me up-to-date on Seaway developments, and he also supplied most of the photographs used in the book.

CHAPTER I

The Geographical Setting

I f you take an atlas from the shelf and look through the first few pages you are sure to find a chart or scale showing the major rivers of the world and possibly one showing the principal lakes. Of the major rivers the Nile, Amazon and Yangtze Kiang are sure to be at the top. You will probably have to go some way down the list to find the St Lawrence. It should be about nineteenth on the list. It is a different story when it comes to the principal fresh-water lakes of the world. Three of the lakes in which we are interested, Lakes Superior, Huron and Michigan, are amongst the six largest lakes in the world. It is obvious that mere length does not make the St Lawrence one of the greatest rivers of the world; it is when it combines with the five Great Lakes that it becomes a great continental waterway. The five Great Lakes, fed by a vast drainage basin, act as a mighty reservoir for the flow of the St Lawrence River. This flow of water from the interior of the continent not only provides tremendous power, both where it becomes concentrated in relatively narrow stretches of the St Lawrence and at intermediate points where water empties from one lake to another, but it also provides a water routeway of over 2,000 miles in length from the Atlantic Ocean to mid-continent.

LOCATION

However, all of these assets would be of small value were it not for the location and orientation of the St Lawrence and the Great Lakes. Many of the world's great rivers (in a physical sense) have not yet been of any great value to man because of their location and orientation. Look at the northern areas of the Soviet Union. Here are several of the longest rivers in the world, three longer than the St

The St Lawrence Seaway

Lawrence, each flowing for over 2,000 miles – but where to? To the Arctic Ocean. Only in the last two or three decades have these rivers proved to be of any commercial value. In North America both the Yukon and the Mackenzie rivers are longer than the St Lawrence, but again they flow northward and through the north-western corner of the continent, an area little developed economically as yet. So length and bigness are of no avail if the river is not suitably located and orientated.

In fact location and orientation may help to compensate for deficiencies. The St Lawrence is far from being a perfectly navigable waterway. There are four major rapids or sets of rapids, as well as narrows and shallow areas. Once into the Great Lakes, there are the Niagara Falls to contend with. These falls and rapids are at one and the same time both assets and liabilities. The falls and rapids can be harnessed for power, but they either have to be removed or circumvented by man-made canals and locks if the river is to be of real value as a commercial waterway. The economic history of the St Lawrence River can partly be told in terms of the four-century-long effort to overcome these many obstacles to navigation.

The Great Lakes–St Lawrence drainage system lies within an area bounded to the west by 93°W. longitude, to the east by 60°W. longitude, to the north by 50°N. latitude, and to the south by 40°N. latitude. The region thus lies due west of an area extending from the English Channel to the boot of Italy. It is not surprising, then, that during the great Age of Discovery, and particularly in the search for a westward passage to Cathay, that the mouth of the St Lawrence should be discovered so early, and provide Cartier, Champlain, La Salle and others with hope that a water route to the 'East' did exist. Dreams of such a route gave way to dreams of a French, and later a British empire within North America, with the St Lawrence and the Great Lakes providing the most direct route into the heart of this continental demesne. The political destiny of North America subsequently became divided, and the St Lawrence River entered into competition with other routes of entry into the continent. Chiefly for this reason the full potential of the St Lawrence has not yet been realised. Nevertheless, because of its location and orientation, the St Lawrence did provide a pathway into the continent first for the French explorers, missionaries, fur traders and other European

I GENERAL MAP OF NORTH AMERICA

settlers who followed. It served as an outlet, too, first for furs and later for timber and especially grain. It is intriguing to contemplate what the economic status of the St Lawrence River might have become under conditions of undivided political control of North America. The region of the Great Lakes–St Lawrence basin, which lies opposite the metropolis of Europe and the British Isles, a densely settled and highly industrialised sphere, was bound to have considerable significance, with the expansion of the metropolis overseas. The fact that the St Lawrence lay immediately to the west, and that it provided the lowest and widest gap through an eastern mountain barrier into a region of vast agricultural resources, meant that in time the St Lawrence–Great Lakes region would be colonised and developed and subsequently enter into trade with the metropolis. The combination of the St Lawrence and the Great Lakes brings Europe within almost 400 miles of direct water contact with one of the greatest grain centres in the world, namely Winnipeg.

In terms of distance from major European ports the location and orientation of the St Lawrence is also advantageous. Via the regular shipping lanes of the north Atlantic Ocean, the distance from Liverpool to Quebec is 2,647 miles, and to Montreal 2,780 miles, compared with a distance of 3,107 miles to New York. Most Great Lakes ports find a shorter route to Europe via the St Lawrence than via New York or other Atlantic and Gulf Coast ports.

Unfortunately, inherent in the location of this great waterway is one of its most serious limitations. The typical climate of a region so located in the north-eastern quadrant of a continental region is commonly described as being of the humid continental short-summer variety. This means a long winter and extreme conditions. Although in the same latitudinal position as western Europe and a part of the Mediterranean, there is no warming effect of a Gulf Stream or North Atlantic Drift, so that average winter-month temperatures are very much lower in the Great Lakes–St Lawrence region. Below-freezing temperatures for at least four months result in the St Lawrence being turned into an iceway rather than a waterway. In contrast, the Canadian Atlantic ports of Halifax and St John and the United States Atlantic ports are ice-free throughout the year. An eight-month navigation season on the St Lawrence and Great Lakes compared with year-round navigation on the Atlantic coast south of the Gulf

Excavation begins on the Seaway downstream from the Victoria Bridge.

1 *Above:* A section of the channel of the St Lawrence has been coffer-dammed.   The waters of the St Lawrence are now being pumped out.

2 *Below:* Excavation and reclamation go on apace during the summer of 1955.

3 *Above:* The entrance to the Seaway. The southern uplifted ramp section of the Jacques Cartier Bridge here crosses the Seaway channel. Reclaimed land and new bridge approaches appear in the foreground, Montreal East in the background.

4 *Below:* Construction under way on the Victoria Bridge. A train of Canadian National Railways crosses a span of the bridge supported by falsework. This span was replaced by a lift span which will enable shipping to enter and leave the St Lambert Lock.

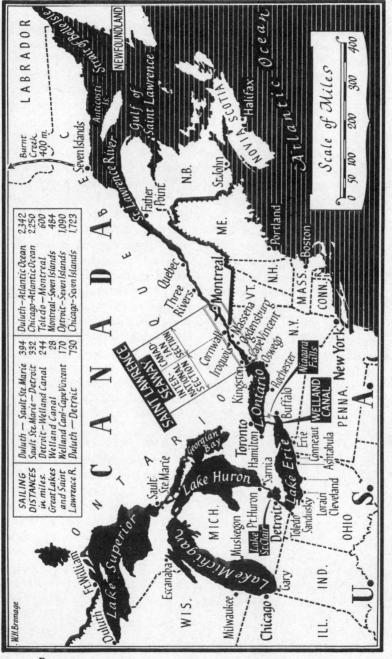

B

. W.H. Bromage

LABRADOR

Strait of Belle Isle

NEWFOUNDLAND

Atlantic Ocean

Gulf of Saint Lawrence

Anticosti Is.

E. Seven Islands

Burnt Creek. 400 m.

St. Lawrence River

Father Point

NOVA SCOTIA

Halifax

N.B.

St. John

ME.

Portland

Boston

MASS.

CONN.

New York

PENNA.

N.H.

VT.

N.Y.

Montreal

Three Rivers

Quebec

CANADA

Massena
Ogdensburg
CapeVincent
Oswego

Cornwall
Iroquois

SAINT LAWRENCE SEAWAY

CANADIAN SECTION

INTER-NATIONAL SECTION

Kingston
L. Ontario
Rochester
Niagara Falls
Buffalo
Erie
WELLAND CANAL

Toronto
Hamilton
Lake Erie
Conneaut
Ashtabula

Georgian Bay

Sault Ste. Marie

Lake Huron

Sarnia
Pt. Huron
Detroit
Lake St. Clair
Toledo
Lorain
Sandusky
Cleveland

MICH.

Escanaba

Lake Superior

Duluth
Ft. William

WIS.

Milwaukee

Muskegon

Lake Michigan

Chicago
Gary

ILL.
IND.
OHIO

U. S. A.

2 THE ST LAWRENCE SEAWAY

of St Lawrence has probably militated against the development of the full potential of the St Lawrence and Great Lakes more than any other factor, even the obstacles formed by numerous rapids and falls. If year-round navigation were possible, deep waterway navigation facilities equal to those in some of the other great canal systems of the world would probably have been provided a century or more ago.

The development of the St Lawrence section of the Great Lakes–St Lawrence waterway must be studied not only in relation to location and orientation but also in relation to the general configuration of the continent, and especially in relation to other routeways leading to the interior of the continent. The North American continent is traditionally divided into four major geological and physiographic units. A vast continental lowland extending from the Gulf Coast to the shores of the Arctic Ocean lies betwixt the high and rugged Western Cordillera, the rugged but not mountainous Canadian Shield, and the Appalachian mountain chain which extends from central Alabama to Newfoundland. The five Great Lakes, Superior, Michigan, Huron, Erie and Ontario, are located within the heart of the interior lowlands, and the St Lawrence River provides an outlet for them to the Atlantic by following a confined course between the southern elevated edge of the Canadian Shield and the northern Appalachians. Before reaching the Atlantic the St Lawrence enters a great embayment in the northern Appalachians known as the Gulf of St Lawrence. There are two relatively narrow outlets from the Gulf of St Lawrence into the Atlantic: the Strait of Belle Isle and Cabot Strait.

Part way through the gap followed by the St Lawrence, in the vicinity of Montreal to be precise, two major tributary routeways branch off from the St Lawrence. The Ottawa River rises to the north-west to the north of the Great Lakes, and in combination with Lake Nipissing and Georgian Bay it provides an alternative routeway to the upper Great Lakes. Until Hudson Bay became the major outlet for Canadian furs the Ottawa route was the lifeline of the fur trade, particularly during the French regime. Schemes for the canalisation of the Montreal–Ottawa–Georgian Bay route to Lake Superior have been proposed frequently as alternatives to the improvement of the St Lawrence and lower Great Lakes route. Directly to the south

The Geographical Setting

of Montreal there exists the only other low-level route across the Appalachian mountain range. This gap is occupied to the north by Lake George and Lake Champlain, which drain via the Richelieu River to the St Lawrence and to the south by the Hudson River. Tributary to this route is another low-level route which lies between the Appalachians and the Adirondack Mountains. This gap is followed to the east by the Mohawk River, which is a tributary of the Hudson River, and to the west by the Oswego River, which drains Oneida Lake. This routeway, commonly known as the Mohawk Gap, in combination with the Hudson River, has provided the St Lawrence route with its most severe competition. As an outlet from the interior of the continent the Mohawk–Hudson routeway has surpassed the St Lawrence because its outlet is the port of New York, which is ice-free the year round. The term 'routeway' is here used in the sense of a low-level land route as well as a waterway, one which can be exploited by rail and road as well as shipping.

Both Hudson Bay and the Gulf of Mexico, in combination with the Mississippi River system, compete as outlets for the agricultural and industrial production of the interior lowlands. Churchill, the port on Hudson Bay, is within 700 miles of the grain-producing Prairie provinces of Canada. When in 1930 Churchill was established as a grain port it was hoped that a considerable proportion of the Prairie export grain would be shipped through this northern port because the combined distance by rail and ocean to Europe was many hundreds of miles less than the alternative routes farther to the south. The Hudson Bay route had won out in the later days of the fur trade, but it was not destined to triumph in the battle for Prairie grain because of a very brief navigation season. Both the Great Lakes–St Lawrence route and the more recently developed route via the Pacific ports of Canada and the Panama Canal have proved superior.

To the south, spread-eagling out over the greater part of the southern half of the interior lowlands, is the Mississippi River system. Although of considerable significance in internal commerce, it has not proved the equal of either the St Lawrence or the Mohawk–Hudson Gap as a major thoroughfare to Europe.

The economic and political history of the St Lawrence can largely be told in terms of its continued competition with alternative routeways from the interior of the continent. In the development of

The St Lawrence Seaway

Canada as a nation the east-west orientation of the St Lawrence–Great Lakes waterway has been of the greatest significance. This waterway has not only provided a path to the interior of the continent, it has also formed a vital link in a series of east-west routeways which bridge the continent. The St Lawrence, the Ottawa, the Great Lakes, the South and North Saskatchewan, the Columbia and the Fraser rivers were followed in turn by the explorer, the fur trader, the miner, the settler and then the railroads. The exploitation and development of this east-west routeway across the continent has enabled Canada to withstand the 'pull' to the south, the economic, political, social 'pull' of a larger, stronger and more fully developed United States of America. From a geographic point of view the major political division of the continent is an artificial one, but both Canada and the United States have developed economically in spite of it. The economies of the two countries have become integrated to a certain extent and both societies have much in common, but they are politically distinct. The ability of Canada to develop as a separate political unit and to maintain a reasonable degree of economic freedom is in no small measure due to the vigorous exploitation of geographic advantages in the form of a natural routeway across the continent which opened up a demesne of bountiful resources, both agricultural and industrial.

THE PHYSICAL CHARACTERISTICS OF THE GREAT LAKES– ST LAWRENCE DRAINAGE SYSTEM

The entire drainage system of the St Lawrence and the Great Lakes covers an area approximately 678,000 square miles in extent. A little less than half of this area lies above the International Rapids section of the St Lawrence, and within it there are 95,000 square miles of water surface on the Great Lakes, namely Lakes Superior, Michigan, Huron, Erie and Ontario. This drainage area is located within three of the major physiographic regions of the continent – the Interior Lowlands, the Canadian Shield and the Appalachians.

With the exception of the peninsula of southern Ontario and parts of the St Lawrence Lowlands the entire drainage area to the north of the St Lawrence and the Great Lakes is occupied by the southern fringe of the Canadian Shield, a rugged, rocky plateau region which occupies the heart of Canada. Tributary rivers, rising as they do in

The Geographical Setting

a great series of glacial lakes along the St Lawrence–Hudson Bay drainage divide, flow south through the upturned edge of the Canadian Shield. These rivers tumble from lake to lake, rush through confined channels and finally empty into the Great Lakes or the St Lawrence. The higher elevations of this southern fringe, ranging as they do from 1,000 feet to a maximum of 3,900 feet, give to the rivers great power, and the glacial lakes which are their source act as a series of vast reservoirs. These rivers are thus ideally suited to development for hydroelectric power. Falls and rapids abound, and it is generally at these points that hydro plants have been located.

Within the Interior Lowlands the divide between the Great Lakes and the Mississippi River system is never much more than one hundred miles from the shores of the Great Lakes. There is thus little drainage and very little power available in this section, other than within the course of the Great Lakes–St Lawrence system itself.

Though elevations within the Appalachians and the Adirondack Mountains are much higher than elsewhere in the drainage basin, the slope to the Great Lakes and the St Lawrence is not a lengthy one so that drainage to the St Lawrence and Lake Ontario is not considerable, nor is power potential significant.

The north-eastern section of the Interior Lowlands, which is occupied by the Great Lakes and a part of the St Lawrence, is formed by a great series of sedimentary rocks, which tend to take a basin-like form and overlap on to the Shield to the north and the Appalachian and the Adirondack Mountains to the south-east. The younger rocks are exposed to the south, while the older rocks are exposed along the edge of the Shield. The surface has taken on the form of cuestas or ridges between lowlands which have been carved out of the weaker rocks. The cuestas, several of which have distinctive escarpments, are best typified by the famous Niagara Escarpment, the most striking landform in southern Ontario. The sedimentary rocks in the basin are of Paleozoic Age and include sandstones, limestones, dolomites and shales. The cuesta or escarpment-forming rocks in the Niagara Escarpment is the Lockport dolomite. This very resistant layer overlies a weak shale, which is eroded very rapidly. The Niagara River drops over the Lockport dolomite and the underlying shale to form the magnificent Niagara Falls and a source of tremendous hydroelectric power.

The St Lawrence Seaway

The Great Lakes occupy sections of the lowland lying between the cuesta formations, though in the case of Lakes Superior and Huron they also extend into the Canadian Shield. The Great Lakes are notable not only for their vast area but also for their depth – Lakes Superior, Michigan, Huron and Ontario extending several hundreds of feet below sea level. Lake Superior is 1,302 feet deep, with 700 feet being below sea level. The comparable figures for Lake Michigan are 923 feet and 343 feet, Lake Huron 750 feet and 170 feet, and Lake Ontario 774 feet and 528 feet. Three agencies probably combined to form the Great Lakes. The major agent was undoubtedly ice. River valleys which existed in the region prior to the last Ice Age were probably deepened by the movement and erosive power of continental glaciers. Many of the outlets of the pre-glacial drainage system have also been dammed by glacial moraine, so that we have here another important agent in the formation of the Great Lakes. The drainage of the Great Lakes basin for a long time prior to glaciation probably took a route partly out to the Mississippi system and partly out to the lower St Lawrence via the Ottawa River. The Great Lakes–St Lawrence drainage system as it exists today is probably an accident of post-glacial times. Crustal warping or uplift or gentle folding of the terrain with the disappearance of the deep and heavy ice sheet also probably influenced the pattern of drainage and the depth of the Great Lakes.

The benefits today of the geological history and especially of the last glaciation are excellent navigation across the Great Lakes and tremendous power potential, especially at Niagara Falls.

From the Great Lakes the drainage of this vast system follows the valley of the St Lawrence through the only substantial gap in the elevated eastern border of the continent. This gap is both an erosive and tectonic feature. For the greater part it is a triangular-shaped structural depression between the Canadian Shield and the Appalachian and Adirondack Mountains. The major tributary of the St Lawrence River, the Ottawa River, also follows a similar feature from the north-west. The geological and physiographic history of the St Lawrence Lowlands is similar to that of the Great Lakes. In addition to the sedimentary rocks, which are here tilted only slightly from the horizontal plane, there are occasional outcroppings of igneous rocks. These outcroppings take their most prominent form

The Geographical Setting

in the Monteregian Hills, a series of distinctive residual peaks, which rise abruptly from the St Lawrence Lowlands to a maximum elevation of almost 1,500 feet. The igneous rocks are also of significance in the channel of the St Lawrence River, where, because of their very great resistance, they have formed the major rapids, such as the Lachine Rapids. The course of the St Lawrence River across alternating resistant igneous rocks and weaker sedimentary rocks has given rise to one of its most distinctive features: the series of lakes or basins which are located immediately below each of the sets of rapids. Lake St Francis is located immediately downstream from the International Rapids section. Lake St Louis is located below the Soulanges Rapids, and the Laprairie Basin lies below the Lachine Rapids. In the settlement of the St Lawrence Lowlands and southern Ontario, and especially in the development of agriculture, glacial and immediate post-glacial times were of the greatest significance, for the soils of the region are largely of glacial origin. During glacial times ice sheets stripped the soils and the vegetation and eroded the surface of the bedrock in areas to the north of the lowlands; then, as the cycle of glaciation continued, this material was deposited as ground moraine to depths of up to 100 feet. This material, commonly known as glacial till, in an unweathered state is extremely dense and resistant, and wherever it was encountered in excavations for the Seaway and the Power projects work proceeded at a slower pace. However, this resistant till did serve as excellent foundation material for Seaway and Power structures.

As a result of the St Lawrence–Great Lakes region being depressed below sea level during the final glacial period, and due to the blocking of old drainage channels by glacial moraine, vast glacial lakes were formed temporarily and the sea invaded certain areas to depths of several hundred feet. A variety of materials, but especially clays, were deposited in these water bodies. Of particular significance are the marine clays of the St Lawrence Lowlands and the Ottawa valley. These deposits in the undisturbed state are relatively stiff, but because of their water content become extremely unstable when they are disturbed. Subsequent to the re-emergence of the land from the sea, beaches were formed and raised to considerable elevations above sea level. Weathering and erosion have since removed much of the loose and soft deposits, and marine clays now, fortunately for Seaway construction, occur only in scattered areas. However, they are of considerable significance agriculturally.

CHARACTERISTICS OF THE RIVER SYSTEM

The St Lawrence River system in conjunction with the Gulf of St Lawrence and the Great Lakes provides a continuous waterway extending 2,347 miles into the heart of the continent from the Atlantic Ocean. For the sake of description and analysis the system can be divided into five distinct sections: the Gulf of St Lawrence, an estuarine section, the lower St Lawrence between a point just below Quebec and Montreal, the upper St Lawrence between Montreal and Lake Ontario, and the Great Lakes.

The Gulf of St Lawrence extends from the Atlantic to the east end of Anticosti Island and covers an area approximately 80,000 square miles in extent. Its waters wash the shores of the Maritime Provinces, Newfoundland and Quebec. There are two passages out of the Gulf into the Atlantic. To the north between Newfoundland and the mainland of Canada the Strait of Belle Isle provides a 12-mile passage at its narrowest part and to the south between Cape Breton Island and Newfoundland Cabot Strait provides a 60-mile-wide passage.

The estuarine section of the St Lawrence commences at Anticosti Island, where it is about 70 miles wide and extends 245 miles upstream to a point at the foot of Orleans Island, where it is only 8 miles wide. Tides obviously diminish with distance inland, but even at Quebec spring tides have a range of 18 feet. For the traveller on the St Lawrence the estuarine section provides most spectacular scenery. For long distances the Laurentian Mountains, which here form the southern edge of the Canadian Shield, and the Appalachians rise abruptly from the waters of the St Lawrence. At Cape Tourmente, 25 miles below Quebec, the Laurentians protrude into the estuary as a rugged 1,800-foot peak, and the mountains immediately beyond it rise to elevations of over 4,000 feet. Farther east the Saguenay fiord opens from the north as a precipitous walled depression in the Laurentian Mountains.

Between Montreal and a point just below Quebec, a total distance of almost 170 miles, the St. Lawrence has an average width of $2\frac{1}{3}$ miles and a very low gradient. In fact it reaches sea level at the exit of Lake St Peter, which is a shallow, 9-mile-wide basin halfway

The Geographical Setting

between Montreal and Quebec. The tidal effect disappears at this point. The narrowest section of the lower St Lawrence is just above Quebec, where the Laurentians and the Appalachians close in on the St Lawrence to confine the river to a ¾-mile-wide gorge-like formation. The city of Quebec obtains its name from the Algonquin expression for 'where the river narrows'. Below Montreal the river drops only 20 feet, most of which occurs between Montreal and Lake St Peter.

Between Montreal and Lake Ontario, a distance of 183 miles, the St Lawrence River falls a total of 246 feet. This section is today without doubt the most significant in the whole of the St Lawrence River. Rapids and lake-like stretches alternate in this section. From the harbour of Montreal, which widens upstream into the Laprairie Basin, the river rises 50 feet in a distance of about 15 miles. The outstanding feature of this section is the Lachine Rapids, one of the rapid formations which owe their origin to the outcropping of resistant igneous rocks in the channel of the St Lawrence. Above the Lachine Rapids Lake St Louis extends for 16 miles to another series of rapids. Just below the rapids the Ottawa River joins the St Lawrence. The Cascades, Split Rock, Cedar and Coteau Rapids form a total drop of 82 feet between Lake St Francis and Lake St Louis. It is here that the St Lawrence is largely diverted through the Beauharnois Power canal. At the upstream end of Lake St Francis, about 30 miles from the Coteau Rapids, the International Rapids section begins. This is a swift-flowing section with a drop of 92 feet in a distance of 44 miles. The channel is relatively narrow and the river finds its way between dozens of small islands.

The Long Sault Rapids are the most famous of the group of four rapids within this 44-mile stretch of the river. The other rapids are the Farran's Point Rapids, the Rapide Plat Rapids and the Galop Rapids. The remaining section of the river up to the outlet of Lake Ontario is known as the Thousand Islands section. The St Lawrence here crosses a southerly extension of the Canadian Shield, known as the Frontenac Axis. The channel is wide and deep and free of rapids.

Within the Great Lakes, from Duluth at the western extremity of Lake Superior to the outlet of Lake Ontario there is a total drop of 356 feet. Lake Superior drains through the St Mary's River and drops a total of 21 feet to Lake Huron, while the only other significant drop is that of the Niagara River, which in flowing from Lake Erie to Lake Ontario drops a total of 326 feet. As mentioned earlier, the Great Lakes are all extremely deep, thus excellent for navigation, but connecting channels have either had to be dredged or by-passed to provide satisfactory navigation. Navigation is today available for a distance of 1,162 miles from the outlet of Lake Ontario to the western extremity of Lake Superior.

It can now be seen that the waters of the Great Lakes and the St Lawrence flow over a series of steps both large and small, and where the fall is considerable tremendous water power is available. The volume of water increases at each step. The average flow in cubic feet per second is 71,000 at the St Mary's River, 174,000 at Lake St Clair between Lakes Huron and Erie, 194,000 on the Niagara River, 237,000 in the International Rapids section, 241,000 in the Soulanges section, and after the St Lawrence is joined by the Ottawa the flow reaches a maximum volume of 262,000 cubic feet per second. The St Lawrence is unique among the rivers of the world in that the tremendous storage capacity of the lakes within the watershed regulates the flow in the river to an unusual extent – the maximum average being about 314,000 cubic feet per second, and the minimum 144,000 cubic feet per second. The variation of about 2 to 1 is in striking contrast to the flow of the Columbia River, with a ratio of 35 to 1, and the Mississippi, with a ratio of 25 to 1.

The relatively uniform annual precipitation within the drainage basin contributes to the uniform flow and the tremendous volume of water in the system. Precipitation varies from 25 to 43 inches, with a mean of 33 inches. Some of the precipitation falls as snow, which varies in annual amount from a mean of less than 40 inches in south-western Ontario to a mean of over 120 inches to the north of the estuary and the Gulf of the St Lawrence. Obviously much of this precipitation is held during the winter in the form of ice. During the winter months over the entire region temperatures average below freezing. In January over the estuary of the St Lawrence air temperatures average below 10°F. This is undoubtedly the cold pole of the region. Ice conditions on the Great Lakes and on the St Lawrence vary a great deal, but ordinarily for two or three of the winter months the greater part of the St Lawrence is completely frozen over, though in the Gulf of St Lawrence there are frequently extensive

The Geographical Setting

areas completely free of ice. If mild air from the Atlantic predominates over the Gulf for lengthy periods ice will not form to any extent. In more recent years ice-breakers have been used on the St Lawrence to break up ice-jams largely in order to prevent serious flooding in the spring. Obviously spring and early summer is the time of maximum flow of the St Lawrence. During the early winter of 1958 and 1959 ice-breakers battled for over a month close to Montreal to free ocean-going steamers which were caught by an early freeze-up of the St Lawrence.

The previous winter the St Lawrence in the Montreal area had not frozen over until late January. Insurance companies take these variations into account and insurance rates on vessels journeying the St Lawrence during the first few weeks and the last few weeks of the navigation season are very high.

From the year 1887 to the present day the average date on which the ship channel between Quebec and Montreal has been open for navigation has been April 17; the earliest date throughout that period was March 19, and the latest May 1. The average date on which the first overseas vessel has arrived at Montreal has been April 24, while the average date of the last departure from Montreal has been December 4. There has been amelioration of conditions during the last decade because during that period the average opening of navigation has been April 12 while the channel has not been closed until December 10. Any hope that improved conditions over the last decade might have heralded a long-term amelioration in winter conditions faded with the winter of 1958–59 which was one of the severest in the last fifty years.

CHAPTER II

Exploration and Early Canals

A 'ROAD TO CATHAY'

The St Lawrence River was discovered and explored by European man in the course of the great search for a north-west passage to Cathay. Wishful thinking had convinced fifteenth- and sixteenth-century cartographers that a short, navigable waterway existed, providing a westward route to the riches of India and China, the Cathay about which Marco Polo had written so enthusiastically. Magellan's voyage of 1519 removed all doubt that America was a continent and that a great ocean lay between America and Cathay. The English and the French, barred from southern routes by the Spanish and Portuguese, ventured to the north-east and the north-west in search of an ocean route to the 'East'.

The Cabots and Verrazano contributed to the map of the Atlantic coastline of North America, but it was left to Jacques Cartier, the St Malo sailor, to venture for the first time far into the continent. Cartier was commissioned by Francis I of France 'to discover certain islands and countries where it is said that he should find great quantities of gold and other valuable things', but there is no doubt whatsoever that Cartier also sailed in hope of discovering a north-west passage. It was not until his second voyage in 1535 that he sailed beyond the Gulf of St Lawrence into the St Lawrence River. Encouraged by the width and depth of the river, but not by the severity of the adjacent landscape, he sailed 1,000 miles into the interior of the continent, only to be halted by the Lachine Rapids and Indian reports of further rapids upstream, as well as the many weeks of journeying still beyond him on the great river. His hope of a passage to the west faded, but he intended to return. However, Cartier was not to return, at least not to a point so far west. His contribution had been made. He had discovered and penetrated a distance of 1,000 miles on the greatest river of the continent. It was as yet too early to visualise the possibilities that lay beyond, but Cartier had established for France the right to the Gulf and the valley of the St Lawrence and the opportunity to occupy the entire continent, an ambition which the French sought to realise for over two centuries but never fulfilled. Apart from his contributions to the map, Cartier was the first of the explorers to carry furs back to Europe. He was also followed into the Gulf of St Lawrence by fishermen, who in turn continued trade with the Indians.

By the end of the sixteenth century, with the fishing industry and the fur trade well established, others in France thought of missions and colonisation, while a few retained the optimism and hopes of Cartier. Amongst the latter was Samuel de Champlain, who was destined to add a great more detail to the map of the Great Lakes–St Lawrence drainage system. In the employ of the Spanish, Champlain voyaged to Spanish America in 1599. It was there that he first heard of the narrow isthmus of Panama that separated the Atlantic and Pacific oceans. On his return to France he suggested to Henry IV the construction of a canal which would 'shorten the voyage to the South Sea by more than 1,500 leagues'. On his first journey to the St Lawrence in 1603, Champlain reached Lachine and gathered an accurate impression of the routeway south along the valley of the Richelieu to Lake Champlain and the Hudson River. He also heard from the Indians sufficient to suggest that great expanses of water lay in the interior and he hoped again of a passage to the Pacific. It was not until July 1615 that Champlain was able to set out on the journey which was to add so much to the map of Canada. A war party of Algonquins and Hurons led Champlain north-westward along what was to become the classic route of the fur trade. They travelled up the Ottawa and Mattawa rivers to Lake Nipissing and down the French River to Georgian Bay. The party then journeyed south via the Severn River, Lake Simcoe and Lake Ontario, towards an Iroquois stronghold near Lake Oneida in New York State. Champlain had probably gathered sufficient information by then to understand the relationship of the Great Lakes to the St Lawrence, but he did not follow this route on his return to Quebec. Although Champlain was never to return into the interior, several of his aides continued exploration within the Great Lakes drainage basin. Some knowledge of the existence and extent of Lake Superior was gained, and a routeway which was eventually to lead to the Mississippi was discovered.

The next chapter in the opening-up of the interior via the St Lawrence was to await the mid-seventeenth century and the exhaustion of the fur-producing areas in the region of the St Lawrence. The Huron and Ottawa tribes had become middlemen in the fur trade between the French and the Indian tribes of the upper Great Lakes. They guarded this right jealously against the attempts of the French to establish direct trade. Early in the second half of the seventeenth century the French managed to make direct contact for the first time with the Indians of the upper Great Lakes. The Ottawa route soon became firmly established as the routeway of the 'coureurs de bois' into the fur-bearing areas of the north-west. Not only was the Ottawa route the fastest and easiest to and from Lake Superior, but it was the only alternative to the upper St Lawrence, which was throughout this period almost continually threatened by the Iroquois, the enemy of both the French and the Indian tribes to the north.

There still remained one link in the Great Lakes–St Lawrence drainage system unknown to Europeans, and this was Lake Erie. Throughout the seventeenth century the hostile Iroquois prevented French expansion to the south. They occupied the Lake Champlain–Hudson River routeway and made the upper St Lawrence and lower Great Lakes a dangerous route to travel. Another of the great French explorers was to bridge this gap. In 1669 Joliet was guided by an Indian south from the upper Great Lakes into Lake Erie, and for the first time it appears that a Frenchman appreciated that the Great Lakes drained into the St Lawrence. Robert Cavalier de La Salle was the first to attempt to exploit this new routeway to the upper Great Lakes. La Salle arrived in Canada in 1667 and took possession of land in the region of the present Lasalle and Lachine on the southern part of the Island of Montreal. The name Lachine, designating both a village and the rapids on the St Lawrence, arose from the name 'La Petite Chine', which was given mockingly to the post occupied by La Salle and his men during the periods between expeditions to the west in search of that elusive route to Cathay. Amongst La Salle's many ventures was the building of the ship *Le*

Exploration and Early Canals

Griffon for use on Lake Erie. He planned to reduce the transport costs of the fur trade by using sailing ships on the Great Lakes rather than canoes on the northern route. Unfortunately, on her maiden voyage *Le Griffon* went to the bottom of Lake Erie with a full load of furs. However, within a decade, other sailing ships were operating on the Great Lakes, connecting military outposts and trading posts. Subsequently La Salle went on to explore the Mississippi–Great Lakes divide and travel to the mouth of the Mississippi. The St Lawrence–Great Lakes region now became linked with the Mississippi basin to provide for the French a strategic zone through the heart of North America.

The St Lawrence River and the Great Lakes had not provided the long-sought passage to Cathay, but they now provided a vital link in the French empire in North America. For the next century the story of this great waterway is one of French efforts to maintain and consolidate this link. The traffic on the waterway was chiefly military supplies and furs, carried in hundreds of canoes and bateaux. The canoes were, of course, traditional Indian bark canoes which varied in size and could carry up to thirty people. They were very strong and light, and could be portaged around the worst of the rapids with relative ease, although in some cases they could ride the rapids. The bateau was a long, flat-bottomed boat, usually 40 feet in length and about 6 to 8 feet wide in the middle. It was made of either pine or cedar, both locally procurable timbers. The great advantage of this boat over the bark canoe was its carrying capacity – 5 tons – and the near impossibility of capsizing it in the rapids, although it could be smashed to pieces on the rocks of the more dangerous rapids. In fact, in 1760 Colonel Frederick Haldimand, who was later to become Governor of Quebec, describes witnessing the wrecking of 46 boats carrying supplies and military stores on rapids in the St Lawrence. Some 84 men were lost at the time and this was a lesson he never forgot, for upon returning to Quebec as Governor in 1778 he immediately suggested the construction of canals. Nevertheless, the bateau had other advantages over the bark canoe. It had a shallow draught, so that it could move in very close to shore. It usually carried masts and sails, an anchor, four men and a pilot as crew. On travelling upstream bateaux were usually dragged over rapids by ropes or men, or unloaded and dragged across portages.

The St Lawrence Seaway

The bateaux remained in widespread use until early in the nineteenth century, when the Durham boat appeared on the scene. The Durham boat combined the light draught of the bateau with superior sailing qualities and much greater carrying capacity. It was flat-bottomed, with a heel and centre-board, rounded bows, a length of 80 to 90 feet, a width of 9 to 10 feet, and a capacity of about 35 tons.

THE FIRST CANALS

The initial canal-building period is generally considered to be the first half of the nineteenth century, because this is the period during which the first 9-foot canal system was completed, but for our first canal, or at least for the first attempts at canal building, we have to go back to the seventeenth century.

It was 1680 when Dollier de Casson, Superior of the Sulpicians in Montreal, first conceived the idea of constructing a canal to connect Lake St Louis with Montreal and by-pass the Lachine Rapids. He planned to exploit the shallow depression which lies between Mount Royal and the Lachine Rapids and which, under natural conditions, was occupied partly by a small lake and river, the Little St Pierre River, which entered the St Lawrence near the present downstream entrance to the Lachine Canal. Construction of this first canal did not commence until 1700. The plan called for a 1-mile-long, 12-foot-wide canal between Lake St Louis and Lake St Pierre. The depth of water was to be $1\frac{1}{2}$ feet at the lowest level of the St Lawrence, which meant that the average depth for the greater part of the navigation season would have been about 3 feet. In addition, the course of the little St Pierre River was to be deepened as far as its confluence with the St Lawrence. A little less than half of the canal was completed before funds ran short and the canal was never finished. However, the completed section was probably used by canoes during the eighteenth century, and possibly other shallow-draught vessels, as this was the main portage route around the Lachine Rapids.

The next serious attempt at canal construction was made soon after Colonel Frederick Haldimand became Governor of Quebec. In 1779 the construction of a series of small locks between Montreal and Lake St Francis was undertaken. Coteau du Lac was the site of the most ambitious undertaking. Started in 1779 and in use by

The St Lambert Lock and the entrance to the Seaway.

5 *Above:* An aerial view of the Seaway channel, the St Lambert Lock, the Victoria Bridge and its lift-span, the Jacques Cartier Bridge (in the background) and the south shore communities of St Lambert and Longueuil on the right of the photo.

6 *Below:* The St Lambert Lock. Length 768 feet, width 80 feet, depth over sills 30 feet.

7 *Above:* Big machines on the job. Work throughout the Seaway and Power projects called for powerful machines that could handle large quantities of rock, clay and sand.

8 *Below:* A giant dredge at work on the Seaway channel. Seventy miles of dredging, amounting to 18 million cubic yards of material, were necessary on the St Lawrence River.

autumn of the following year, it was patterned after early efforts in Great Britain and was the first lock canal in North America. It was 900 feet long and 7 feet wide. The three locks it contained were each less than 40 feet long, while their depth of 2.5 feet was just sufficient for the passage of bateaux. Twenty years later these locks were enlarged to permit a brigade of six bateaux to pass at once.

During the first half of the nineteenth century political and economic developments caused serious consideration to be given to the construction of a canal system throughout the Great Lakes–St Lawrence system. By 1800 settlement of the upper St Lawrence Valley and other parts of southern Ontario was well under way, and American settlers were moving beyond the Appalachians into the Ohio country and the Middle West. The new settlers in what had become known as Upper Canada had supplies to carry in, and later agricultural produce for export. An early journal describes the difficulty of transportation on the upper St Lawrence at this time. Supplies were carted from Montreal to Lachine and there put on bateaux or Durham boats, which travelled in 'brigades' of five or six across Lake St Louis. At the Cascades Rapids three-fourths of the cargo was discharged and carted to the head of the Cedar Rapids. The remaining load was locked past the Cascades and dragged up the Split Rock and Cedar Rapids. The boats were then reloaded and locked past the Coteau Rapids, and went hence across Lake St Francis to the Long Sault Rapids, where there were two locks. Again, three-fourths of the cargo had to be unloaded and hauled overland. Rapids farther upstream called for similar treatment. From Prescott boats either sailed or were towed to Kingston. The complete journey from Montreal to Kingston for an average cargo took twelve days. Even this time was an improvement over a decade earlier. Improvements were made in the river itself, a channel being cleared through the Soulanges and Lachine Rapids to allow boats to sail down loaded and be pulled up light. The above time was reduced gradually over the next decade or two. In 1809 the first steamship appeared on the St Lawrence, travelling from Montreal to Quebec in three days instead of the usual fifteen to sixteen days taken by sailing vessels. The success of steam on the lower St Lawrence was followed by the construction of the first steamship on the Great Lakes and its use after 1818 between Kingston and Prescott. Steamships subsequently found their way on to Lakes St Louis and St Francis, and by 1833 they were so improved that they were able to travel up the Long Sault and the other rapids on the upper St Lawrence. Where portages were necessary, four-horse coaches carried passengers. This was an improvement, but it was still not good enough to handle the traffic, which rapidly increased in volume.

Not only were the colonists exceedingly anxious that these many handicaps on the St Lawrence be overcome, for they wished easier and cheaper means by which to send out their products and bring in supplies and new settlers, but the merchants of Montreal also desired a good navigable waterway to the interior. Initially the merchants were interested in the upper St Lawrence and Great Lakes as an alternative to the Ottawa–Georgian Bay fur trade route, but with the union of the two great fur trading companies, the North West Company and the Hudson's Bay Company in 1822, the St Lawrence lost its significance in the fur trade. The cheaper route by Hudson Bay won out in the first of the great economic battles fought by the St Lawrence.

The merchants of the lower St Lawrence now sought fresh fields of trade. In the growth of southern Ontario and the Middle West they saw an opportunity to restore the system that had been the basis of earlier economic development. They appreciated that the St Lawrence offered the shortest route between Europe and the interior of the continent. Again the merchants of Lower Canada could become the middlemen in a trade which would comprise incoming manufactured goods from Britain and Europe and outgoing agricultural and forestry products, and possibly even minerals. The merchants not only needed a good navigable waterway in and out of the interior, but they also needed the combination of a free market in America and a protected market in Britain. Under Britain's mercantile system American agricultural produce exported via the St Lawrence route would benefit from the preferences that Britain extended to trade from colonial areas. Ports such as Montreal and Quebec would thus profit at the expense of American ports. The merchants also hoped that the return trade in manufactured goods would be funnelled through Quebec and particularly Montreal.

For various reasons, some external and some internal, the St Lawrence did not rapidly develop as the great highway of commerce dreamed of by the merchants of Lower Canada. Canada did not capture the trade of the Great Lakes region and the Middle West as anticipated for several reasons. The United States sought to set up a protective system and Great Britain set about abandoning mercantilism and the colonial preference. Neither of these measures took serious proportions until later in the century, but they were always threatening. Rivalry between Upper and Lower Canada also hindered progress. The people of Upper Canada were generally interested in the development of the St Lawrence, but they also desired the right to trade via the United States if an American route to Europe offered them cheaper transportation. In Lower Canada the French, who were in the majority in the legislatures, were opposed to a government undertaking what they claimed would chiefly benefit the English merchants.

The development which really retarded the development of the St Lawrence was the construction of the 7-foot-deep Erie Canal in 1825 between Albany and Buffalo. This canal exploited the only other lowland route across the Appalachian mountain system. It followed the Mohawk Valley from the Hudson River and then cut overland to Lake Erie. The Erie Canal could only handle barges, so that transhipment was still necessary; but with labour cheap, transhipment charges were not prohibitive. A new route was now available for Middle Western grain. At New York there was a port open all the year round, in contrast to Montreal and Quebec, which were closed for several months of the year. Upper Canada also appreciated the benefits of the new route for both imports and exports.

However, at the same time the Erie Canal provided an example to the Canadians of the advantage of canalisation. The Erie Canal had been completely paid off within nine years and it had brought prosperity to cities along its banks as well as to New York. These advantages were particularly obvious to the Montreal merchants, who saw in the canalisation of the St Lawrence an opportunity for Montreal to emulate New York.

By the time the success of the Erie Canal was obvious some improvements in the canalisation of the St Lawrence and the connecting channels of the Great Lakes had already been made. An extremely significant treaty had also been signed by the United States and Britain. The Webster-Ashburton Treaty of 1824 opened the St

Lawrence and the Great Lakes to free navigation by the United States and Canada. The war of 1812 increased interest in canals on the St Lawrence. It was appreciated that sound defence depended upon good communications. As the war ended, Lower Canada legislated to build a canal at Lachine Rapids, but nothing was done about it. Three years later, in 1818, the governments of Upper and Lower Canada appointed a joint committee to report on the advisability of building canals on the St Lawrence above Montreal. The report was favourable, and in 1821 the government of Lower Canada appointed a commission to undertake the construction of a canal between Lachine and Montreal. The first Lachine Canal was opened to navigation in 1825. It had a depth of 5 feet and could accommodate vessels with a 4½-foot draught. There were seven locks, each 100 feet by 20 feet.

A by-pass of Niagara Falls was first suggested in 1798, but the construction of the first 7-foot Welland Canal was not commenced until 1824. It was opened in 1832. Private interests were responsible for this construction, but financially the endeavour was unsuccessful and the canal was taken over by the Canadian Government in 1831. Most of the capital available for investment in canal construction came from England. The investors were more prepared to loan to governments than to individuals, so that canal construction in the future was all to be undertaken by government.

Although canals around some of the other rapids on the St Lawrence were commenced prior to 1841, it was not until that year and the union of Upper and Lower Canada that the full resources of the two Canadas were put behind the canalisation of the St Lawrence. The action that now took place was largely due to what was perhaps the earliest Seaway lobby, the Association for the Improvement of the St Lawrence. The arguments put forward by this group are those which have been repeated in every campaign for an improved canal system. In 1832 one proponent stated, 'Our burdens can be removed, and our prosperity insured, only by constructing a ship canal of not less than eight to ten feet depth of water; and thus rendering Lake Erie's territories and the shores of the upper lakes on the same level, a sea coast.'

The Cornwall Canal around the Long Sault Rapids was the first of the new canals on the St Lawrence to be started – in 1834; and it was the first completed – in 1843. It was 9 feet in depth. The first canal around the Soulanges Rapids, the Beauharnois Canal, was commenced in 1842 and completed in 1849. The four canals, jointly known as the Williamsburg Canals, which by-passed the four rapids between the Long Sault and Prescott, were commenced in 1843 and completed in 1847. Between 1843 and 1848 the first widening of the Lachine Canal was undertaken. The depth was also 9 feet and the width 80 feet. The Welland Canal had been deepened to 9 feet in 1841, so that by 1848 a ship drawing not more than 8 feet of water could avoid the rapids on the St Lawrence and the Niagara Falls. By 1855 it was possible for a vessel with the same draught to sail into Lake Superior. In that year the State of Michigan completed a canal with a double-lift lock around the St Mary's Falls.

The first canal-building period was over, but it was by no means a complete success.

THE 14-FOOT CANAL

The 9-foot canals of the St Lawrence and the Great Lakes were outmoded before they were completed. Ships on the Great Lakes and on the lower St Lawrence had increased in size so rapidly, particularly with the coming of the steamship, that the shallow, 9-foot canal system was an uneconomic waterway. Only the smaller ships and barges could be used, so that a considerable amount of tranship-ment was necessary. The early success of the Erie Canal continued, and trade through the eastern seaboard ports of the United States increased tremendously. These ports also became a market of considerable proportions for imported goods and they thus had a large amount of shipping available for the export trade at relatively low rates. The agricultural produce of the West moved along the Erie Canal route in ever-increasing quantities. In spite of the shorter distance to European markets, freight rates between Montreal and Liverpool were higher than between New York and Liverpool. Winter freezing of the St Lawrence, the narrowness of much of its channel, and fogs in the Gulf of St Lawrence all contributed to curtail seriously the commercial growth of the St Lawrence route.

On top of all this, in 1845–46 the United States Government, in legislation commonly known as the 'Drawback Acts', made it possible for Canadians to export grain to Britain and Europe via New York without the payment of duty. There was thus a complete reversal of the expected turn of events, and instead of United States grain being shipped via the St Lawrence to Britain, Canadian grain started to move via New York. The measure which was chiefly responsible for this reversal was, of course, the abolition of the Corn Laws and the repeal of other mercantilistic legislation. An outlet via Canada could no longer offer any great advantage to the American exporter.

As the second half of the nineteenth century began, the prospects of the St Lawrence canal system were not at all bright, and the enthusiasm of the seaway proponents cooled off temporarily. The cost of construction had been tremendous. A total of $20 million had been spent by governments and private investors, and considering the population, which was somewhat less than two million in 1850, this sum was a far greater financial burden than any Canadian Government has been prepared to face since. The country had staked a considerable proportion of its resour:es upon these early canals because it was felt to be a matter of life and death for the economy. By and large, the results of all the efforts and sacrifice that went into these first canals were extremely disappointing.

Worse was still to come. By 1850 the railway era was under way in Canada. At this stage the few short lines existing were ancillary to the canals, but after 1850 there was a rapid increase in railroad construction. The Grand Trunk, built between 1852 and 1863 from Chicago through Toronto and Montreal to Portland, Maine, was the most direct competitor of the Great Lakes–St Lawrence waterway. This railroad and others built in both Upper and Lower Canada at this time were intended to draw the traffic of the Middle West down the St Lawrence Valley, as were the St Lawrence canals. The railways were soon in possession of the cream of the traffic, leaving the canals as a distinctly secondary means of transportation. A specialisation tended to develop with bulk commodities, especially grain and coal, moving along the canals, while the railways carried the rest, especially manufactured goods. But at the existing depth of 9 feet the canals were not adequately equipped to handle even the bulk commodities.

From the mid-nineteenth century the railways had first call on government financial support, but, nevertheless, soon after Confederation the Federal Government inaugurated the second major period of canal construction. In 1870 a Royal Commission was set up to study the canals of the country and to make recommendations. The report of the Commission, published in 1871, recommended a 12-foot deep canal from Lake Superior to Montreal as well as the construction of a canal from Baie Verte (Quebec) to the Bay of Fundy, presumably to avoid late ice and fog in the Gulf of St Lawrence. An additional recommendation called for the completion of canal connections from Ottawa to Lake Champlain. The first canal on the Richelieu River, which drains Lake Champlain into the St Lawrence, was constructed between 1831 and 1843, around St John, but Canada's first railroad, built in 1836 between La Prairie and St John, served the same purpose, so that the canal was not a success It is significant that this Commission considered that the canal system should not be concerned solely with capturing the American trade of the Middle West, but that the system should be prepared to handle an ever-increasing traffic, particularly in grain, from the Canadian Prairie provinces, as well as a substantial interprovincial trade within eastern Canada. However, the Commission still considered competition with the Erie Canal as well as the New York railroads a major objective of an improved canal system. By 1860 virtually all the grain of the American Middle West moving eastward, both for domestic consumption and for export, was transported by the Great Lakes and Erie route, but the railroads were annually carrying an ever-increasing share of this grain. By the 1880's the Erie Canal was considered virtually obsolete, so that the competition was now between the New York railroads and the Canadian railroads and canals.

The first major improvement of the canal system was the deepening of the Welland Canal to 14 feet in 1887. It had already been deepened to 10 feet in 1853. Meanwhile, in the lower St Lawrence the navigation channel between Montreal and Quebec had been deepened to 20 feet, so that the canal system between Montreal and Lake Ontario formed a real bottleneck between the Atlantic and the upper Great Lakes. Improvements of the connecting channels between the upper Great Lakes began with the construction of a canal around the St Mary's Falls in 1855. In 1871 the United States Government began an improvement programme, and by 1881 they had deepened the canal to 16 feet. They had also constructed a second route through the Weitzel Lock, to a depth of 18 feet. In response to the rapidly developing traffic in grain and iron ore the United States continued its improvement programmes, and in 1896 opened the Poe Lock, a single, 21-foot-deep lock, while the canal was deepened to 25 feet. Almost simultaneously the Canadian Government constructed a 22-foot draught canal and an 18-foot, 3-inch-deep lock parallel to the U.S. facilities. By the end of the century deepening of the Lake Michigan–Lake Huron–Lake Erie connections had been completed to a depth of 20 feet, and specialisation in ship construction for the bulk handling of grain, iron ore and coal was well advanced.

Even prior to the report of the Canals Commission in 1871 a deepening programme had commenced on the Lachine Canal, but here, as at other points on the upper St Lawrence, work was carried out in a spasmodic and half-hearted manner, so that it was not until 1903 that the deepening programme was sufficiently completed to permit the opening of a continuous system of navigation of 14 feet depth from Montreal to Lake Erie. Deepening and widening of the Lachine Canal commenced in 1863 and was completed by 1884. A draught of 17 feet was provided in the two lower locks to enable the movement of fully loaded vessels in and out of the Wellington Basin, a turning basin which is a part of the port of Montreal. The remaining three locks were 14 feet deep, 270 feet in length and 45 feet in width. The canal was 8¾ miles in length, and the five locks raised or lowered shipping 46 feet. The locks built at this time were not replacements for the old locks, they were new locks and were built alongside the old ones. Both the 9-foot and the 14-foot systems survive to the present day.

Between Lake St Louis and Lake St Francis the Soulanges Canal was constructed on the north bank of the St Lawrence to replace the 9-foot Beauharnois Canal on the south bank. Both canals provided a by-pass of the Cascades, Cedar and Coteau Rapids. The new canal was started in 1891 and completed in 1899. The length was 15 miles, and the depth 15 feet. Five locks raised or lowered shipping a total of 84 feet.

The improvement of the Cornwall Canal took much longer. Work commenced in 1876 on the straightening of the canal, but lock installation was not completed until 1900. The canal was 11 miles long, with proportions similar to those of the other canals. Six locks provided a total lift of 48 feet. The completion in 1903 of the Farran

Exploration and Early Canals

Point, Rapide Plat and Galop canals, collectively known as the Williamsburg Canals, provided the final link in the 14-foot canal system. These canals covered a combined distance of 13 miles and provided a total lift of 31 feet.

Before the new canal system could be considered as ready for full-scale commercial operation, accessory improvements were essential. By the turn of the century, the lakers being built for grain shipment were of too large a draught for the Welland Canal. They were specialised vessels, smaller but similar in design to the big lakers of today. Many could carry 10,000 tons of cargo in bulk form. Thus at the upstream end of the Welland Canal it was necessary to provide the proper facilities for the berthage and unloading of these upper lakers as well as adequate storage facilities. These were provided by 1908. At the Montreal end similar elevators and loading facilities were brought into service in the same year. Two years earlier the channel between Montreal and Quebec had been deepened to 30 feet, so that Montreal now ranked as a first-class ocean port.

Whereas it could justifiably be claimed that the earlier 9-foot canal system was obsolete by the time of its completion, a similar claim for the 14-foot canal system would have been somewhat premature. In 1871, when the Canals Commission recommended a 12-foot canal system below Lake Erie and a few years later when it was decided to deepen it to 14 feet, there was already on the upper Great Lakes a considerable amount of shipping with a draught greater than 14 feet. By 1904 there was obviously a great deal more, so that on these grounds it could be argued that the 14-foot system was obsolete by the turn of the century. However, the outcome of the building of the 14-foot canals was by no means as much a disappointment as that of the 9-foot canals. Canada entered a period of rapid expansion from 1900 to the outbreak of the First World War. The population in the St Lawrence Valley and southern Ontario increased very rapidly as a result of industrialisation, the exploitation of water power and agricultural expansion.

For the Canadian Prairies the first decade of the century was a boom period. High prices, lower production costs on the farm resulting from mechanisation and higher yielding varieties of grain, and lower transportation charges produced a condition of unprecedented prosperity for the Prairie farmers. The reduction in transportation

41

charges was made possible by an increase in the use of special grain carriers on the Great Lakes and the removal of all tolls upon the Welland and St Lawrence Canals in 1903. In 1899 the Canadian Pacific also cut its rates on export grain to Fort William. An increasing volume of grain consequently moved eastward to the St Lawrence ports via the St Lawrence canals.

By 1895 two large steel mills were operating in Canada, one at Hamilton and the other at Sault St Marie. The iron ore and coal consumed at both plants was moved on the Great Lakes. Large quantities of iron ore from the Mesabi Range shipped from Duluth and Appalachian coal from Lake Erie ports provided the bulk of the traffic through the Welland Canal.

The 14-foot canals, at least during the first decade or two of their existence, could be considered as commercially successful. However, even greater economies would have resulted, particularly for the grain trade, if greater depth of the canals had obviated transhipment at Port Colborne.

In no small degree the obsolescence of the Erie Canal contributed to the early success of the 14-foot Welland and St Lawrence Canals. The 14-foot canal system did not succeed in capturing even temporarily any sizeable portion of the Middle Western grain trade, but at least the Erie Canal was no longer a threat to the Prairie–St Lawrence route. The St Lawrence route did not succeed in diverting Middle Western grain because the Erie Canal route was too well established. As the canal failed to cope with the grain trade, the railways following the same route took over, and accessory facilities – storage elevators, loading and unloading equipment – were expanded, particularly at Buffalo and New York. Consequently, transport charges were kept at a minimum. However, by the turn of the century, largely as a result of the rapid improvement in western agriculture after a long depression, even the Erie Canal and railroads combined were barely capable of handling the grain flowing in their direction. It appeared, as a result, that New York might be losing its commercial supremacy, and the opening of the 14-foot navigation on the St Lawrence threatened a serious new blow to its trade. In 1895 New York State had decided to deepen the Erie Canal to 9 feet, but the project collapsed because of inadequate finance. With the first serious talk of a really deep waterway on the St Lawrence at the end of the century New York State resolved in 1903 to construct an entirely new canal, 12 feet deep with locks 328 feet in length and 45 feet in width. However, construction of the canal proved to be a long and costly business, and it was not fully completed until the mid-twenties, although some limited navigation was possible from 1917. No provision was made for swing bridges, so traffic was restricted to barges. The long delay in improving the Erie Canal system was undoubtedly beneficial to the St Lawrence Canal system, although the Erie route never lost its pre-eminence amongst the grain routes to Europe.

If certain economic developments in Canada and the tardiness of New York State in improving the Erie Canal system aided the commercial development of the Welland–St Lawrence canal system, at the same time they stimulated the expansion of railroads in Canada between west and east in an attempt to provide a shorter, more practicable and cheaper route to St Lawrence, Atlantic and Pacific ports for western grain. The National Transcontinental Railway, first suggested in 1903, was to be a joint endeavour of the Canadian Government and the Grand Trunk Railway Company. This railway would join Winnipeg to the port of Quebec, providing an alternative outlet for western grain and a stimulus to northern development. The line was completed in 1913, but it failed in its major objective. It was also planned in 1903 that one of the existing Prairie railway systems would be extended both to the Pacific and also linked up with the proposed National Transcontinental Railway. At the same time the Canadian Government gave its support to the Canadian Northern Railway Company, which planned to establish itself as what would have become a third transcontinental railway, by constructing lines westward to the Pacific from its existing system in the Prairies and eastward to Quebec and on via New Brunswick to Nova Scotia. These proposals were later modified and some proposed construction was abandoned.

Symptomatic of the prosperity and optimism of this period is the fact that even while the Federal Government was extending aid and encouragement to the railroads, almost as if entirely unmindful of the future needs of the proposed railways for traffic, it authorised detailed surveys of a proposed Ottawa River–Georgian Bay canal. This authorisation, made in 1904, called for a canal capable of handling the large upper-lake freighters, which would have shortened the distance to Montreal considerably and have reduced transport charges even more so because of the elimination of transhipment at any intermediate point. A few years later the Government also approved the survey of a new route for a new and larger Welland Canal. It was not clear for some years whether the Government intended to proceed with the construction of both canals or choose one route. A change of government took place in 1911, and the new Conservative government decided on the construction of a new Welland Canal to a depth of 25 feet. Accordingly, work commenced in 1913. It appears that the Welland proposal was chosen in preference to the Ottawa River–Georgian Bay route because of an estimate of five years for the construction of the former as against ten years for the latter. As it turned out, it was not until 1932 that the Welland Canal was completed. There were many reasons for this long delay. Activities were suspended for a time during the First World War, and then during the twenties technical difficulties were encountered in excavation. The final canal was almost twice as deep as the old Welland Canal. It had eight locks in place of twenty-six, and each lock was much longer and could be operated more rapidly. The new canal permitted the grain carriers of the upper Great Lakes to reach the entrance to the upper St Lawrence, where Prescott rapidly developed as a second transhipment port. Port Colborne, though, did not decline markedly because many of the larger carriers would not enter the Welland Canal due to the amount of time involved in passage through the canal with its eight locks and to the relatively narrow channel which cut the speed of the carriers considerably. Thus some transhipment was still necessary. On the upper Great Lakes further improvements were made at Sault Ste Marie. A third American canal and lock, the Davis Lock, with a depth of 22 feet, was completed in 1914, and a fourth, the Sabin Lock, with a similar depth, was opened in 1919.

The final improvement of the Great Lakes–St. Lawrence Canal system was the construction of the 31-foot-deep MacArthur Lock at Sault Ste Marie, which was opened in 1942. The construction of the MacArthur Lock required the destruction of the Weitzel Lock, so that in 1942 there were four American and one Canadian locks at Sault Ste Marie.

Exploration and Early Canals

These latter improvements did not, of course, result in competition for the 14-foot St Lawrence canals; rather, they greatly increased commerce on the Great Lakes and highlighted the deficiencies of the St Lawrence Canal system. Even the great burst of railroad construction, including the line from Winnipeg to Churchill, a port on Hudson Bay, during the first three decades of the twentieth century, did not immediately provide any significant competition. Severe competition might have been expected by the new railways constructed eastward from the Prairies to Quebec, but this did not materialise.

The significant development which did eventually provide competition for the Great Lakes–St Lawrence route was the construction of the Panama Canal. This major achievement, of course, furnished a new ocean route for the transportation of grain from Vancouver to European ports. However, any considerable diversion of traffic to this route depended in large measure upon the reduction of railway rates on grain from the Prairies to Pacific ports. These rates were reduced in 1925 and grain from Alberta, particularly, began to flow to the Pacific ports of Vancouver and Prince Rupert for Asia and Europe. This westward movement increased gradually, and by the early 1950s Vancouver had become Canada's major grain-exporting port.

It has been stated that the development of the western outlet for grain provided competition for the Great Lakes–St Lawrence route, but there were periods when this outlet also provided relief for the Great Lakes–St Lawrence route. In fact there have been navigation seasons, particularly more recently, when the 14-foot canal system was physically incapable of handling more grain than it did. It should also be pointed out that on the average only about half of the grain exported from the Pacific ports is bound for Europe.

It now appears that there were two major criticisms which could be levelled against the 14-foot St Lawrence Canal system, or, in other words, it had two major shortcomings. The first criticism, one which was made even before the canal system was completed, was that too small a percentage of the world's shipping could use the canal at a depth of 14 feet, which meant a draught of 12·5 feet. Two types of vessels used the St Lawrence canals. The most important was the 'canaller', which was designed with a flat keel and special structure to navigate the 14-foot canals and carry a maximum tonnage of bulk cargo. The typical and maximum proportions of the 'canaller' were 254 feet in length, 44 feet in width, with an average dead weight tonnage of 2,500 tons. The speed of the 'canallers' averaged 9 to 10 knots. Most of these vessels operated between Montreal and Prescott or Port Colborne, but some went as far as the Lakehead. The other type of vessel was the typical small ocean-going cargo ship, built in Europe to trade directly between Europe and Great Lakes ports. These ships did not appear in the canals until the 1930s, when the first regular cargo service between Europe and the Great Lakes was inaugurated. The maximum dead weight capacity is between 1,800 and 2,000 tons. They normally have a length of 250 feet, a breadth of 42 feet and a fully loaded draught of about 16 feet. As a result of this deep draught, many of these ships have to traverse the canal system with a cargo short of maximum capacity and load up at Montreal or some other lower St Lawrence port. Quite obviously the canals were suited to a specialised traffic, namely bulk commodities carried by specially designed 'canallers'. With a 2,000 ton ocean-going freighter as the upper limit of the St Lawrence Canal system, there was but a small percentage of shipping arriving regularly in North American ports which could have entered the 14-foot canal system. However, there is no certainty that great numbers of ocean-going freighters would have flocked into the Great Lakes if the canal system had been deepened. This point will be discussed at greater length in the final chapter.

The other major shortcoming of the St Lawrence canals was the slowness of passage of the majority of vessels using the system, due to the narrowness of the canal and the great number of locks. There were 41 miles of canalised water and 22 locks providing a total lift of 209 feet. Apart from the slow passage there were other limitations. The proportions of the locks and the canals varied. The controlling features of the St Lawrence Canal system were those of the smallest canal and lock. The limiting lock within the canal system was Lock 17, situated at Cornwall on the Cornwall Canal. Length and depth were standard, but the minimum width was 16 inches less than that of all other locks in the system. As well, Lock 17 and Lock 15 of the Cornwall Canal had a capacity appreciably less than either the Soulanges or the Lachine canals. The main reason was that at Cornwall these two lower locks were very nearly in flight, with very little pondage between, thereby rendering the feeding of water rather slow. At the upper end of the Morrisburg Canal there was trouble caused by the short approach wall and the sharp cross-current. A Canadian engineer reported in 1927 that 'The most that could be done through Locks 15 and 17 of the Cornwall Canal is probably 40 to 42 lockages per day, the almost maximum. The freest canal, the canal with the largest capacity, is the Soulanges, completed in 1900. Its capacity can be estimated at about 14,000,000 tons of freight per year. I think we can assume that the Soulanges Canal can actually take care of about 60 to 70 boats every 24 hours.'

The maximum capacity of the canal system was that of Locks 15 and 17, and it was estimated to be about 9,000,000 tons a year, which was approximately the average total downbound tonnage, during the final few years of operation of the 14-foot St Lawrence Canal system. This maximum was also approached in 1928 and again in 1937 and 1938.

It was thus obvious that the St Lawrence Canal system was used to capacity as long ago as 1928. The average annual tonnage of cargo subsequently varied considerably, but in most years the canal system was able to handle all scheduled shipping without too much trouble. However, this is not to say that the canal system was satisfactory. There is no doubt that ship-owners would have placed a greater amount of shipping in service on the canal system if a rapid passage could have been assured.

CHAPTER III

The St Lawrence Seaway and Power
Projects – The Idea

By the time the St Lawrence canals were all improved to a depth of 14 feet a movement for a much deeper canal system was already under way. By 1903 the completed canal system was outmoded in certain respects. Both lake ships and ocean ships had grown so rapidly in size with the use of steam and iron that only a small percentage of the upper Lake and sea-going freighters could navigate the 14-foot canal system. Imagine how pitifully true this was in 1958, when the International Rapids section of the 14-foot system was used for the last time.

There is no certainty as to when a deep seaway (for the purposes of this discussion – 20 feet or more) was first suggested. By the turn of the century two locks at Sault Ste Marie had been constructed to depths of over 20 feet and one canal to a depth of 25 feet. This development resulted directly from the phenomenal increase in the production of iron ore in the Mesabi range. Unfortunately this great increase in the importance of Great Lakes navigation had little influence upon the St Lawrence system. Nevertheless, for other reasons, sufficient interest was aroused in a deep-water seaway between the Great Lakes and the Atlantic for the United States and Canadian Governments to appoint a Deep Waterways Commission in 1895. The Commission was directed to report on all possible waterways which might connect the Great Lakes and the Atlantic. It is to be observed immediately that by the very terms of this Commission the battle between the St Lawrence and the Erie Canal was by no means over. When the Commission reported two years later they concluded that 'both the St Lawrence and the Mohawk Canal route were possible', but they recommended that connections between the

Great Lakes first be improved. This initial report was the first of many to report favourably on a deep-water seaway, and it immediately prompted the organisation of an anti-Seaway lobby in the United States, a lobby which waged battle successfully for fifty-nine years.

Why was the construction of the St Lawrence Seaway as it exists today opposed so successfully for so long? It never ceases to amaze many living within the continent, and many more without, that the 14-foot St Lawrence canal system was retained for so long. Surely the construction of a deep waterway was justified much earlier in the century? What arguments were there for the construction of a deep waterway? Who argued for the project in the United States and Canada?

ARGUMENTS FOR

It is obvious from the construction of deep locks and canals in the upper Great Lakes by the turn of the century that both governments appreciated the economic advantages of Great Lakes navigation. Whether judgment is based on no more evidence than a map of North America, one can hardly escape the conclusion that improved navigation on the entire Great Lakes–St Lawrence system was a blessing to all. All the arguments put forward earlier for canalisation still stand, and perhaps gather strength, for surely with the continued economic development of the interior of the continent direct water access to mid-continent, and cheap transportation at that, became even more important. The St Lawrence route was still shorter than the Erie Canal route to the Atlantic and Europe, and the latter was never more than a barge canal, so that in no sense did it open the Great Lakes to the ocean shipping of the world. The Mississippi never was really in the race when it came to any fair proportion of the transatlantic trade.

Has there ever been a sound economic reason for the construction of the Seaway? This question could be answered as Stephen Leacock once answered it, 'To hell with economics; it's a magnificent conception, and has got to be built.' Unfortunately, though thousands agreed with this argument, it was obviously not sufficiently persuasive to swing the balance in favour of a Seaway! A 'magnificent conception' is not necessarily an economic proposition. Here probably lay the greatest weakness in the Seaway argument. There was probably no sound economic case presented for the Seaway until the Iron Ore Company of Canada commenced producing Quebec-Labrador iron ore for the furnaces of the Middle West. In addition, the argument that water transportation is the cheapest form of transportation, particularly on a route which is obviously the most direct route between the mid-continent, the St Lawrence valley and Europe, is not necessarily sound. Obviously it is the cheapest form of transport to a shipowner, whose ship can ply the Seaway with a full cargo each way without paying tolls, and can switch to another trade route while the system is closed to navigation for four to five months of the year. But somebody has to pay for this convenience, for undoubtedly it is a form of subsidised transport. The argument for cheap water transport was often linked with the claim that rates by water acted as a national restraint on railway freight charges, and there is no doubt that this is true. It is rather obvious, then, where much of the opposition to the Seaway came from.

For three-quarters of a century the group which has most consistently sought a shorter and cheaper route to Europe has been the grain producers. One of the earliest and most vocal demands for a deep waterway came from western grain producers during the latter half of the nineteenth century, when they were faced with dropping prices in the midst of a world-wide depression. They sought their solution in cheaper freight rates. The action of the United States and Canadian Governments in 1895 in setting up the Deep Waterways Commission was partly a result of this demand. As economic conditions improved and grain prices rose the cry became less vocal. Again in the early twenties and during the depression of the thirties pressure from the agricultural core of the continent was considerable, but not sufficient to have the project undertaken. However, it was during those two periods that Seaway proponents came closest to success. When the Seaway proponents were finally closing ranks in the early 1950s for their final onslaught, the reduction in grain freight rates was again a potent argument, particularly in Canada.

Although the first hydroelectric plant was completed in the International Rapids section at Massena, New York, in 1901, the Seaway project was not seriously associated with power development until 1914. In that year the United States suggested to Canada that the

International Joint Commission might study 'the question of development of boundary waters for navigation and power'. Canada was not interested at this stage, for war in Europe was imminent. However, in 1918 a Canadian parliamentary 'Committee on Waters and Water-Powers' suggested the possibility of developing power on the St Lawrence, and in the same year the New York and Ontario Power Company applied to the International Joint Commission for permission to develop power at Waddington, New York. They applied again in 1921, but were not refused a licence until 1933. Another private concern, Hugh L. Cooper and Co., representing du Pont, General Electric and Alcoa, sought a licence to develop, by means of five dams, power amounting to 6,625,000 h.p. at an estimated cost of $1,450,000,000. They offered to provide navigation facilities free to the governments of the United States and Canada in return for the power rights. It does appear doubtful that there is that much power in the International Rapids section, but the request for the licence provides some indication of the amount of money a private utility was prepared to spend on the scheme. At least by this time the argument had obviously become one for a Seaway and Power project, and with this merger the idea gathered strength, but also more opponents.

The major advantage to accrue from the merger was the very great reduction in the cost of the construction of the deep waterway. Without the deep water of a power pool much more channel excavation and many more locks would be necessary. For the proponents of one or the other of the projects there were disadvantages as well. It is difficult to say whether they outweighed the advantages or not. Whereas there was never any question as to who would be the authorities responsible in the United States and Canada for the improvement of navigation facilities, there was considerable controversy over who would be responsible for the development of power. In the United States, as the power would chiefly be used in New York State, the state rather than the Federal Government would be responsible. The state could choose between a specially created authority or a private utility company. The former was preferred, and in 1931 the New York State Legislature established a Power Authority. By the Power Authority Act of that year full development of the International Rapids section by the State of New York was authorised.

The act created history, because this was the first power authority set up in the United States by either the Federal or a state government.

In Canada the rights of the provinces had not been as clearly established as the rights of the states in the United States, and the proposal for the development of power in an international waterway gave rise to a controversy between the Federal Government and the provincial governments, especially Ontario and Quebec. Accord was not reached until 1932, and in that year provision was made for the province of Ontario, through its Hydro-Electric Power Commission, to develop power in co-operation with the Power Authority of the State of New York.

When the suggestion of power development in the International Rapids section was first made there appeared to be insufficient demand for power in the region to justify the undertaking. Even as late as 1928, in replying to a request of the United States that the two governments should enter into negotiations for the development of the combined project, the Canadian Government suggested delay in the construction of the International Rapids section until Ontario could absorb the power developed there. It was not clear that there was really sufficient demand in upper New York State, but the proponents of the Power project stated that they could find the customers without much trouble. The bid by du Pont, General Electric and Alcoa to develop the power themselves in the early twenties was evidence that private capital was interested and that a market could be created. This has been borne out by the most recent developments. Both General Motors and Reynolds Aluminum have already established large plants adjacent to the Barnhart Powerdam.

When the governments of New York State and Ontario did finally agree on the development of power, the United States Government withheld the necessary permission, arguing that the Seaway project would have a much better chance of approval if it remained tied to the Power project. For the same reason the Canadian Government would not give Ontario the 'go-ahead'. So for the better part of two decades the demand for power could not be satisfied until the proponents of the Seaway won their battle.

Power Projects – The Idea

Around whom or what did the proponents of the Seaway and later the Seaway and Power project rally in the United States and Canada? The most effective and influential organisation to lobby in the United States for the Seaway was probably the Great Lakes–St Lawrence Tidewater Association. Formed in 1919, it was one of the predecessors of the Great Lakes–St Lawrence Association, the most recent Washington lobby. The Tidewater Association was chiefly responsible for bringing the United States and Canadian Governments together to discuss the Seaway issue for the first time. Support for the organisation came initially from Minnesota, Wisconsin and Michigan, and later from states in the Middle Western interior and as far afield as California and South Carolina. Some of these states established state commissions to promote the Seaway cause, and funds were appropriated for their support, as well as for the support of the Tidewater Association. The Tidewater Association gave considerable support to its Canadian counterpart, the Canadian Deep Waterways and Power Association, which was also founded in 1919. As one Canadian authority has stated, 'This Canadian association, however, has never been anything more than a pale simulacrum of the Great Lakes–St Lawrence Tidewater Association and has never displayed one-tenth of the activity or exercised one-tenth of the influence of its counterpart in the United States; indeed it has placed considerable dependence on the latter body for material and assistance in the conduct of its case.' The United States association gave considerable support to the Seaway cause in Canada in 1924 when one of its representatives traversed the Prairie provinces organising support for the St Lawrence Deep Waterway Association of Western Canada. A number of investigations and reports covering both the United States and Canada were also sponsored by the Tidewater Association. One such report, *Economic Aspects of the Great Lakes–St Lawrence Ship Channel* by R. S. MacElwee and A. H. Ritter, was the first of many excellent, comprehensive surveys which presented a case for the Seaway.

The Great Lakes–St Lawrence Association, the successor of the Tidewater Association, though finally meeting with success, for a long time lacked support on a nation-wide scale and carried on a rather limited operation in favour of the Seaway. It never received support from a national organisation such as its opponent lobby, the National St Lawrence Project Conference, received from the Association of American Railroads. It was only during the final two or three years of the Seaway 'battle' that the Great Lakes–St Lawrence Association became a really effective lobby.

There were other organisations founded from time to time in both countries to promote the cause of both the Seaway and the Power projects. They served varying purposes and met with varying degrees of success. Some represented regional interests, some attempted organisation on a national scale. Some were concerned solely with the Power project. Some produced useful reports, which were used as evidence in parliamentary debates, while others concentrated on the personal approach to influential members of the governments in the United States and Canada. These organisations undoubtedly all served a useful function.

Both Federal Governments from time to time appointed commissions or committees specifically to investigate the Seaway and Power projects. The United States St Lawrence Commission, appointed by President Coolidge in 1924, submitted several reports in favour of the immediate construction of both the Seaway and the Power projects. One of the strongest pleas made for the combined project was that made in 1926 by the St Lawrence Commission in its first report, widely known as the 'Hoover Report'. Herbert Hoover, Chairman of the Commission, was then Secretary of Commerce in Coolidge's government. The Canadian counterpart of the St Lawrence Commission, the National Advisory Committee, reported to the Canadian Government in 1928, but although it indicated agreement in principle with earlier United States recommendations it did not present a strong case for either the construction of the Seaway or the Power project at that time.

Following the failure of the United States Senate to ratify the 1932 Seaway Treaty, a Seaway Council was created in the United States to promote interest in the Seaway and Power projects. President Roosevelt was largely responsible for its creation, and he particularly urged its active co-operation with the Power Authority of the State of New York, which was, of course, interested in the development of St Lawrence power.

Power Projects – The Idea

Practically every major United States Government department study from the early 1920s to 1954 claimed that the project was a necessity. The United States Department of Commerce, especially, made repeated claims for the Seaway on economic grounds. From a 1927 estimate of 19 to 24 million tons per year of available commerce they reached a maximum estimate of 84 million tons in 1948. Even the more conservative estimates of the Canadian Department of Trade and Commerce, which reached a maximum of 44 million tons, were strong arguments for the Seaway.

Finally but not by any means the least of the rallying points for Seaway and Power project proponents were the Presidents of the United States, from Wilson to Eisenhower. Wilson, Harding, Coolidge, Hoover, Roosevelt, Truman and Eisenhower all said the Seaway was a 'must'. In 1914 Wilson's government reaffirmed the International Boundary Treaty of 1909 and called on the International Joint Commission, created by the Treaty in 1909, to study the question of a Seaway and Power project on the Great Lakes and the St Lawrence. In Harding's message to Congress in 1922 he submitted a report of the International Joint Commission, which favoured the St Lawrence for both navigation and power development over other waterways suggested. His government attempted in the same year to negotiate a treaty on the basis of this report, but was rebuffed by Canada.

President Coolidge was responsible for the creation of the St Lawrence Commission, a body which was predisposed to a report in favour of the project by the very nature of the appointments to membership. All the members were either avowed advocates of the project, such as Mr Herbert Hoover and Mr Craig, the Executive Director of the Great Lakes–St Lawrence Tidewater Association, or were representatives of industrial concerns or other organisations which would undoubtedly be interested in the construction of a Seaway or a Power project.

President Hoover made his first public pronouncement of advocacy of a deep waterway in 1920. He campaigned actively for the project and the Presidency during the twenties and was elected President of the United States in 1928. He then used his authority to seek a Seaway and Power Treaty with Canada. This treaty was signed in Washington in 1932, a few months before Mr Hoover moved out of the White House.

The St Lawrence Seaway

President Roosevelt, prior to his elevation to the Presidency in 1933, was Governor of New York State. In that position he was chiefly responsible for the enactment of the Power Authority Act of the New York State Legislature and the settlement with the Federal Government of the question of allocation of cost and control of power development on the St Lawrence. As President he failed in his attempt to have the 1932 Treaty ratified, but he worked vigorously throughout the thirties to find a way of overcoming opposition to the projects. He made a final serious attempt during 1941 and 1942 to obtain Congressional approval by means of an Executive Agreement, urging construction of the projects as a war measure. Approval was not forthcoming.

In every 'State of the Union' message President Truman delivered to Congress he recommended construction of the project. During his seven years in office his pleas became increasingly vigorous. It was during this period that the project argument gathered strength and Canada threatened to 'go it alone' if the President could not obtain Congressional approval.

When President Eisenhower came to office in 1953 the 'writing was already on the wall'. The defence argument was now called upon to turn the tide and the President was able to affix his signature to the Wiley-Dondero Act, Public Law 358, in the 83rd Congress, in 1954.

It is difficult to identify in Canada any outstanding champions of the Seaway and Power projects until towards the end of the 1940s. There were certainly prominent individuals who spoke out from time to time in favour of the project, but no major public figure championed the cause as Hoover and Roosevelt did for so long in the United States. Between 1921 and 1950 Canada had three Prime Ministers, but only two remained in office for any length of time. These gentlemen were Mr MacKenzie King and Mr R. B. Bennett. During MacKenzie King's first two terms as Prime Minister between 1921 and 1930 the Canadian Government succeeded four times in bringing project negotiations with the United States to an indecisive termination. It was not until the election campaign of 1930 that he publicly stated for the first time that he favoured the construction of the Seaway. When MacKenzie King took office for the third time in 1936 the Seaway issue was pushed into the background because of concern with more pressing economic measures, but by

Power Projects – The Idea

1941 his government was prepared to sign the Executive Agreement with the United States. At the same time his government reaffirmed their agreement with Ontario on the development of power on the St Lawrence. From the end of the Second World War his campaign for the project was intensified, and in 1949 he was quoted as saying that the value of the project was so great as to call for serious consideration by Canada of the possibility of the development of at least the power phase of the project by Canada alone. Within a year his Secretary of State for External Affairs, Mr R. B. Pearson, went further in saying, 'It might also be advisable for Canada to look into the possibility of building at the same time a Canadian deep waterway on our side of the border.'

By 1950, the year of MacKenzie King's death, the United States and Canada were within four years of complete agreement on the Seaway and Power projects, but it is difficult to claim for this distinguished Canadian Prime Minister any great measure of credit for this achievement. It might almost be true to say that project proceedings went this far in spite of Mr King, and that it was a strong Conservative Ontario government, of whose supporters a fair proportion voted Liberal in Federal elections, which applied the pressure on Mr King and his government because of the necessity of an additional major source of power in Ontario.

Mr Bennett's enthusiasm for the project was also half-hearted. In the election campaign of 1930 he also pledged his party to the construction of the St Lawrence Seaway, and on behalf of the government he formed in that year he later signed the 1932 Treaty. Unfortunately all discussion of the Treaty in Parliament was delayed until such time as the United States Senate should ratify the Treaty, and this was not done during Mr Bennett's term of office. Thus Mr Bennett and his government were not called upon to present in detail their case for the Seaway and Power projects. One suspects that the campaign promise of 1930 was not pronounced seriously, and even the Treaty signing was a good risk because Mr Bennett was well aware of the strong opposition to the Treaty in the United States.

OPPONENTS GALORE

No sooner was the first Seaway proposal made in the United States in 1895 than opposition appeared in the form of an anti-seaway

57

lobby. To the Canadians it was just another proposal in a long line of proposals for the improvement of navigation on the St Lawrence. The organisation of opposition to the Seaway project and later the Seaway and Power projects in the United States is an excellent example of how a Washington lobby or pressure group works. In more recent times the various elements of Seaway opposition were brought together by a central organisation known as the National St Lawrence Project Conference, or, as it was subtitled, 'A Nation-wide Organisation in Opposition'. In 1950 there were more than 250 organisations listed as members of the Conference, and the most powerful of these was the A.A.R., the Association of American Railroads. The A.A.R. has a standing policy of opposing any form of competing transportation that requires government subsidy.

From the very beginning the railroads of the eastern United States have opposed the Seaway. It is to be remembered that the Pennsylvania Railroad also opposed the construction of the Panama Canal, and still complains about it, while the New York Central still complains about the New York State Barge Canal. It is also to be remembered that railroad companies in the United States are not transcontinental, that the eastern railroads are confined to the eastern half of the continent. The New York Central, for example, reaches no farther west than St Louis, Missouri. The eastern railroads are the railroads which undoubtedly face competition from the St Lawrence Seaway. Whether or not this competition will actually result in the loss of traffic to the railroads, only the future will show. The western railroads have not remained neutral in the fight, because as members of the A.A.R. they support that organisation's policy of opposition to subsidised transportation, even though they themselves were at one time subsidised heavily by means of lavish land grants. In contrast to the eastern railroads, they are not competing directly for traffic. If the Seaway lives up to expectations their traffic should increase. The A.A.R., chiefly on behalf of the eastern railroads, argues that if the current estimates of future traffic on the Seaway are fulfilled, then the eastern railroads would no longer earn an adequate income. In 1948 the United States Department of Commerce estimated a maximum 84,278,000 tons of traffic for the future Seaway, and it was this estimate chosen by the A.A.R. for their argument, regardless of the fact that later more realistic estimates averaged less than 50 million tons. The A.A.R. maintained that the railroads would lose revenue to an amount of approximately $200 million. A substantial percentage of this loss would result from not hauling traffic, traffic which would probably only result from industrial expansion, particularly around the Great Lakes, as the result of the completion of the Seaway. They also claimed a loss from not hauling coal that would probably have had to be used for electricity in upper New York State, if power had not been developed. The A.A.R. also argued at the same time that the estimate of the Department of Commerce was fantastically high and that the increase in Seaway traffic would be so slight that the expenditure necessary would not be justified.

It has already been pointed out that one of the arguments that finally swung the balance in favour of the Seaway was the need for cheap haulage of Quebec-Labrador iron ore, and iron ore will make up a high proportion of future Seaway traffic. Most estimates of future iron ore tonnage range between 30 and 40 million tons, and most of this ore will be used by the Middle Western iron and steel centres, so that for these blast furnaces Seaway ore will be cheap, as compared to ore brought overland from Baltimore, Philadelphia or Contrecoeur, a transhipment point near Montreal. One 1958 estimate of relative transportation costs of ore indicates that the Seaway charge will be approximately one half of the combined ocean and rail haul from Seven Islands, Quebec, to the Pittsburgh and Middle Western centres. Of course, if the Seaway had not been constructed there is no certainty that the railroads would have been given the privilege of hauling that amount of ore. The iron and steel industry is well established on the Atlantic Seaboard, so that rather than face the high cost of transportation to the Middle West the industry might well have preferred to increase capacity at the seaboard. The eastern railroads have claimed that the Middle Western steel companies want the Seaway built, whether they use it or not, simply to drive down railroad rates. There are some steel companies that are not immediately interested in Quebec-Labrador ore because they still have substantial reserves in Minnesota, but they rely on Great Lakes transportation of their ore.

The anti-Seaway and Power project battle was not fought by the railroads alone. Members of the A.A.R. included Atlantic and Gulf

59

The St Lawrence Seaway

Coast ports, coal companies, railroad labour, mineworkers, many private utilities, many private industrial concerns, towns large and small, and states that would be affected adversely by any reduction in rail traffic and the opening up of the Middle West to cheaper overseas imports. Particularly during the twenties and thirties there was also opposition from an anti-British and isolationist Middle West. The anti-British insisted that a Seaway would open up the Great Lakes to the British Navy.

The Washington lobby, the National St Lawrence Project Conference, operated on behalf of all these groups. They not only organised the opposition in the two houses of Congress, the Senate and the House of Representatives, but they also disseminated anti-Seaway literature with such titles as 'Iceway' and 'The Great Delusion', and organised anti-Seaway meetings across the country. The lobby combined the criticism, the arguments of all anti-Seaway groups, into one powerful argument which was successful from 1895 to 1954.

The case for the railroads has already been presented. The Atlantic and Gulf Coast ports feared the loss of traffic as much as the railroads, but there was little logic in their claim that they would decline in importance with the diversion of some Middle Western and western traffic to the Seaway. New York did not decline with the development of Albany as a deep-water port. Cities as large and industrialised as New York, Baltimore and Philadelphia do not, by any means, depend economically upon their port function, although without doubt it has been very significant in the development of all three cities. Some industries might decline in importance, or others, such as the iron and steel industry, might not expand as rapidly as without a Seaway. It would probably be in the interests of the United States to decentralise industry a great deal more, even at the expense of the east, so if the Seaway stimulates further industrial development in the Middle West it will be to the advantage of the nation as a whole.

The argument of the Gulf Coast ports, particularly New Orleans and the Texas ports, is even weaker. Traffic from the Middle West, likely to be diverted from these ports to the Seaway, is but a fraction of today's total traffic. In the future the bulk of the freight handled at these ports will result from continued industrial and agricultural development in the South, as well as from the import trade. New Orleans has long battled for a larger share of the western and Middle Western agricultural export trade, but has only recently made any progress. Even if New Orleans loses this trade to the Seaway it will not seriously affect her port function.

Coal companies opposed both the Seaway and the Power projects. They argued that if the railroad traffic in the east declined, then there would be a further reduction in the consumption of coal, already drastically reduced by the conversion of the railroads to diesel. The coal companies' opposition to the Power project appeared a little more justified. If power had not been developed on the St Lawrence for use in upper New York State and Ontario, a greatly increased number of coal-burning thermal electric plants would have had to be installed to provide the necessary power. Coal companies have been fighting hydroelectric power development for many decades, but experience shows that industrial development based on hydroelectric power frequently results in an increase in the consumption of coal. This was certainly so in the case of hydro development by the Tennessee Valley Authority (T.V.A.), although any increase in coal consumption in the St Lawrence Valley would not be for precisely the same reasons. Coal-burning thermal electric plants were first installed in the Tennessee Valley as stand-by plants, due to the extreme fluctuations in the flow of the Tennessee River, which at the Wilson Dam in northern Alabama amounts to a maximum 115 times greater than minimum flow. Such stand-by plants will not be necessary on the St Lawrence because of the regularity of flow. The power pool on the St Lawrence has reduced fluctuation from $2 \cdot 3 : 1$ to $1 \cdot 7 : 1$.

In the case of railroad labour and mineworkers, their sympathies obviously lay with their employers. Many private utilities – i.e. those companies privately producing and distributing electric power or distributing power produced by municipal, state or federal authorities – opposed the Power project on the grounds that they should be allowed to develop the power themselves, and, as we have already seen, several private companies earlier in the century did seek licence to develop the International Rapids section. Private utilities are particularly afraid that the St Lawrence Power Project will turn out to be another T.V.A., in spite of the agreement made in 1930 between the Federal Government and the Power Authority of New York that the power would be distributed by private utilities. The power phase of the T.V.A. development has been opposed strongly by private utilities because in its rapid, widespread and successful development of electric power it has obviously encroached on what the private utilities consider to be their demesne.

Apart from the anti-British and isolationist opposition to the Seaway in the Middle West, there was also opposition to the Seaway and Power projects because certain Middle Western regions feared that these projects would result in a restriction in the amount of water that could be diverted from Lake Michigan for industrial and domestic purposes. This diversion is extremely important to cities as large as Chicago that use tremendous quantities of water for industrial and domestic purposes. Water is also needed to maintain 9-foot navigation on what is known as the Sanitary and Ship Canal which connects the Chicago River to the Illinois Waterway, which in turn leads to the Mississippi River. The maximum amount of diversion has been limited by law, but requests have recently been made to the United States Government for this limit to be raised. With the power development now complete any future increase in diversion will probably have to result from diversions into the upper Great Lakes, such as the diversion which has already been made by Canada from the Hudson Bay drainage area.

Disapproval of the project by states and cities was chiefly voiced through Chambers of Commerce. In fact more than half the members of the A.A.R. were Chambers of Commerce, scattered throughout the eastern half of the United States. A small community in Maine might oppose the project through fear of reduction in railroad traffic, while another in Arkansas or east Texas might voice disapproval in sympathy with the Gulf Coast ports. In some communities or states there were conflicting interests. Southern New York State was concerned about the future of the port of New York, while upper New York State wanted cheap electric power. A New England Council represented the opposition in New England, but communities in north-western Vermont hoped to share cheap St Lawrence power and even gain some benefit from the Seaway if their own water connections with the St Lawrence were improved. Communities on the shores of the Great Lakes obviously did not always share the sympathies of mining communities farther south. These states' Congressmen and Senators had a somewhat difficult task, but it is clear that the influence of the older urban, industrial and mining centres away from the shores of the Great Lakes dominated the actions of their Congressional representatives for a very long time.

THE PRELIMINARIES – LEGISLATION

Before discussing the final stage of the battle, in which the supporters of the Seaway and Power projects gained ground at the expense of the anti-Seaway lobby, it will be well to summarise the legislation, the treaties and the submissions made by commissions and conferences which finally paved the way for the creation of the authorities responsible for the construction of the St Lawrence Seaway and Power project.

The year 1895 has already been recognised as the year in which the United States and Canada first gave recognition to the possible need of a deep waterway into the interior of the continent. In that year a Deep Waterway Commission was appointed by the governments of the United States and Canada. The following year the United States created an International Waterway Commission to study the feasibility and usefulness of a deep-water canal between the Great Lakes and Montreal. The conclusions of the Deep Waterway Commission which were presented in 1897 have already been commented upon.

The first definite recommendation was made in 1900 when a United States Board of Engineers on Deep Waterways suggested an all-American waterway of 21-foot depth. No further action was taken until 1902, when the President of the United States invited the British Government to join in the formation of an International Waterways Commission to deal with the Seaway project. This commission was established the following year and held its first meeting in June of 1905. Meanwhile, a Canadian Order in Council in 1903 had accepted an offer from the United States to investigate and report on conditions and uses of waters adjacent to the boundary line between the two countries. In the same year the Canadian Premier urged construction of a waterway connecting the Great Lakes and the sea. In 1909 an International Boundary Treaty was signed, which established the International Joint Commission of the United States and Canada, which supplanted the earlier Waterways Commission.

The St Lawrence Seaway

The Joint Commission was given certain jurisdiction as well as advisory powers. One of its first tasks was to consider the requests of two companies interested in developing power on the St Lawrence in the Long Sault region. The next request from the United States for action came in 1914, but Canada did not reply because war in Europe was imminent.

Largely as a result of the activity on the part of the Great Lakes–St Lawrence Tidewater Association, the International Joint Commission began hearings in 1920 to determine the views of representatives of commercial and other organisations on the advisability of the construction of a deep waterway and the development of power on the St Lawrence. In the same year several unsuccessful requests were made by private utility companies to the International Joint Commission for licences to develop power on the St Lawrence.

The first of a long series of favourable reports to be made by the International Joint Commission was made in 1921 to the governments of the United States and Canada. In the same year the Ontario Hydro-Electric Power Commission and a United States private company made recommendations to the Commission on the development of St Lawrence power, while a New York State Commission made a preliminary report on the 'St Lawrence Ship Canal'. One of the first detailed economic reports was also submitted to the Commission. It was a year of activity which laid the foundation for the next important move on the part of the United States. In May of 1922 on the basis of a report of United States and Canadian engineers and the International Joint Commission, the United States expressed readiness to negotiate a treaty, but Canada replied by declaring it needed more time to study the reports. At the same time the Ontario Provincial legislature unanimously passed a resolution favouring the project.

President Coolidge in his annual message to Congress in 1923 again strongly urged the construction of the Seaway. Canada again expressed a desire for a more detailed study, and recommended an enlarged Joint Board of Engineers. The United States agreed, and the result was a report in 1926. They estimated the cost of a 25-foot channel and full-scale power development at between $625 and $650 million, but they could not agree on the details of construction. The United States favoured a single-stage power development with

9 The Laprairie Basin Seaway Channel. The bottom width of the channel is 300 feet. Dykes, reclaimed land, turning basins and the foundations of the new Champlain Bridge can be seen in the background.

10 Excavation for a highway tunnel under the Seaway at Beauharnois. A total of 51 million cubic yards of rock had to be excavated during the construction of the Seaway.

a powerdam at Barnhart Island, the scheme which was finally adopted, and the Canadians favoured a two-stage development, with dams near Morrisburg and Cornwall.

Another report in the same year indicates that the St Lawrence as a deep waterway route still faced some competition. The Chief of Engineers of the United States Army presented a report titled 'Waterway from the Great Lakes to the Hudson River'. Fortunately the Hudson River alternative was rejected. Early in the next year the President of the United States again presented an urgent plea to Congress, and a note was subsequently sent to the Canadian Government, but again Canada expressed a wish to postpone negotiations, this time until its National Advisory Committee had reported in full. This committee reported a year later, and proposed a 27-foot-deep channel as well as the proposals already presented for the development of power. They included the Welland Canal as a purely Canadian component. Canada now replied to the 1927 United States note, but suggested a delay in the construction of the International Rapids section development until Ontario was in a position to absorb the power developed there. The United States in turn objected to this delay and also to the suggestion that the cost of the old St Lawrence and Welland canals be included unless they were to be used in the new project. A Canadian Order in Council of the same year highlighted another problem Canada faced in clearing the way for negotiation with the United States. The controversy between federal and provincial authorities over power development rights was referred to the Supreme Court of Canada. The decision handed down by the Supreme Court in the following year was inconclusive. In 1930 the United States Government again informed Canada that she was ready to proceed with the proposed development of the St Lawrence Seaway.

The years 1931 and 1932 provided new hope that United States and Canada might negotiate. The Joint Board of Engineers agreed on a two-stage development with a dam at Crysler Island, and the New York State legislature created a Power Authority to negotiate with the United States Government over the development of St Lawrence power. Accord was also reached between the Canadian federal government and the provinces of Ontario and Quebec in the controversy over power rights. The long-awaited treaty was signed by Canada and the United States in Washington on 18th July 1932. A two-dam system and a 27-foot channel were agreed upon. In February of the following year a Senate Committee on Foreign Relations recommended approval of the treaty, subject to certain amendments. In April the United States House of Representatives confirmed agreement between the United States Army Corps of Engineers and the Power Authority of the State of New York, which paved the way for a final inter-departmental investigation of the project. The report of this committee was transmitted to Congress in 1932 by President Hoover, with a message urging ratification of the treaty. The axe did not fall until two years later when the Senate failed to ratify the treaty, now at Roosevelt's request. A roll-call produced a majority for ratification, but not a two-thirds majority, which was necessary for approval.

Throughout the remainder of the 1930s President Roosevelt continued active campaigning for the project. Early in 1936 he stressed the need for a new approach to the treaty, which would include full consideration of the problems of the Niagara River. The full power potential of the Niagara River and the famous falls had not yet been utilised. Two years later, at the dedication of the Thousand Islands Bridge, President Roosevelt again stressed the advantages and warned of dangers in delaying the construction of the Seaway and Power projects.

A 'Seaway Council' was organised in the United States in 1936 to create interest in the project and to support it with the active co-operation of the Power Authority of the State of New York. Meanwhile, other groups were actively opposing construction. Typical of these was the 'Niagara Frontier Planning Board'.

The year 1940 was marked by considerable activity in the International Rapids section and the appearance of another strong argument for both the Seaway and the power. Special defence funds were allocated by the President for preliminary engineering surveys and investigations, and in his annual message to Congress he urged action immediately because of the value of the project to national defence.

An Executive Agreement was signed in Ottawa six months later by the United States and Canada, providing for construction of the works in the International Rapids section and for completion of the navigation improvements in other sections of the Great Lakes–St

Lawrence system by 1948. On the same day the Canadian Government and the province of Ontario renewed their 1932 arrangement that Ontario would operate the Canadian share of the project and reimburse the federal government by payment of an allocated share of construction costs. Similarly, an agreement was reached between the United States Government and the Power Authority of the State of New York. In June of the same year, 1941, the President urged Congressional approval of the Executive Agreement. The following year, after various House committees had approved the agreement, President Roosevelt came close to ending the Seaway argument once and for all by using his personal wartime powers in the form of an Executive Agreement, but again no action resulted. Evidently faced with a shortage of funds to which he had immediate access, President Roosevelt was forced to seek them from the Army. Unfortunately the Army considered the project as 'insufficiently urgent as a wartime project'. Following this rebuff, the President, at a press conference, indicated he had no immediate hope of action in construction of the project, due to shortage of steel and manpower. With the death of President Roosevelt in 1945, the Seaway and Power projects lost a great champion. No one man had fought so long and had come so close on so many occasions to seeing Congress ratify the project treaty.

When President Truman came to power in 1945 the argument was growing stronger, although as yet it was by no means certain that the Seaway and Power projects would be under way before the end of the decade. In fact even as late as 1950 Carrol B. Huntress, the chairman of the National St Lawrence Project Conference and Vice-President of Republic Coal and Coke Co. of New York, claimed on behalf of his Washington lobby, 'We're going to hold the line. My motto is, "They shall not pass".' That Mr Huntress was proved wrong and within such a short time was largely due to one major economic development on the continent, one constructive idea on the financing of the Seaway, and the near desperation of Ontario, particularly, but also of New York State faced with supplying electric power to a rapidly increasing population and expanding industries.

Claimed by one proponent to be 'the first constructive idea about the Seaway in twenty years' was the suggestion which was made in committee in the United States Congress in 1946 that 'the collection of tolls for self-liquidation of the project be authorised'. Although charging tolls was contrary to Canadian national policy, the Canadian Government was so anxious for action that it agreed to the charging of tolls. The opposition was not impressed with this concession. They argued that the increase in traffic as a result of improved navigation would be so light that the annual revenue from tolls could hardly pay for annual maintenance, let alone amortization. The agreement on tolls by the United States and Canada was based on the following estimates of various United States and Canadian government departments. The estimated annual maintenance and operating costs of the Seaway were $3,500,000 and the annual cost of amortization over fifty years $11,100,000. The estimate of annual charges which would have to be met by tolls would thus amount to $14,600,000 a year. It was further estimated that on the basis of potential annual traffic of between 40 and 50 million tons toll charges of between 30 and 40 cents per ton of cargo would be sufficient to meet the annual operating costs of $14,600,000 for Canada and the United States of America. In a report to the United States House of Representatives the United States Army Engineers stated that 'toll charges within these ranges appear readily subject to absorption by the prospective commerce without any danger of loss of the movement to other trade channels. The committee is therefore convinced that the revenue potentials of the Seaway are ample to assure that it can be made self-liquidating'.

The important economic development which gave considerable weight to the above claim and to the Seaway argument in general was the discovery of very extensive and rich deposits of iron ore on the northern Quebec-Labrador border. The discovery of such large amounts of ore resulted from a vigorous exploration programme, initiated in 1942 largely in response to the dwindling supplies of high-grade hematite iron ore of the Lake Superior fields. By 1949 400 million tons of hematite ore had been proven, which was considered to be the necessary minimum reserve to justify full-scale development. The convenience of this discovery to Seaway proponents obviously lay in the fact that via the Seaway the Quebec-Labrador ore could be easily and cheaply transported in huge quantities to the steel centres of the Middle West.

How desperate was the need of the Middle Western centres for an alternative or additional source of ore? In 1952 the United States

National Security Resources Board made the following statement: 'In recent years the Lake Superior region has supplied approximately 85 per cent of the total iron-ore requirements of the United States. Since the beginning of 1940 we have shipped from the Lake Superior region a total of 770 million tons of ore. Of this total nearly 600 million tons came from open pit-mining operations, an amount which by common agreement is about equivalent to the entire remaining reserves of direct shipping and easily treated open pit ores. Assuming something less than peak operations in the steel industry over the next decade and making no allowance for growth in consumption resulting from increased population these open pit reserves at the end of the period will be seriously reduced. Twenty years from now production cannot be even half as large as at present.'

However, the steel industry could by no means assume 'something less than peak operations over the next decade'. The United States population had been increasing rapidly, the cold war was showing no signs of abating, so that alternative sources of ore had to be sought and in large quantities. One alternative, and the one supported by opponents of the Seaway, was the possibility of obtaining vast quantities of iron through the beneficiation of low-grade magnetic taconites. Taconite has an iron content of about 25–35 per cent, a percentage comparable with the Jurassic ores of Britain, France and Belgium. Reserves of taconite are placed at about 5·5 billion tons (1950 date) of iron-bearing material. It is estimated that these taconites can provide about 1·7 to 1·8 billion tons of iron concentrates of 60 to 65 per cent iron content. Many years of experimental work and substantial sums of money have been devoted to the development of processes of concentrating these taconites. There is now little doubt that a practical and economic method will be developed for making iron concentrates, but in the immediate pre-Seaway era there was no plant in operation producing iron suitable for blast-furnace use, and no commercial installation had yet been started.

HUNGRY FURNACES

The second alternative was the increased use of foreign ores, especially Quebec-Labrador ore. The United States National Resources Board in 1950 estimated that the United States dependence on imported ores would rise to approximately 18 million tons in 1955, to

25 million tons in 1960, and to approximately 48 million tons in 1970. In the light of recent development it is now appreciated that these estimates were extremely conservative. In 1957, the year of the recession, the United States imported approximately 16 million tons of ore, with 12 million tons originating in Quebec-Labrador. Nevertheless, these estimates were sufficient to make a strong argument for the Seaway, especially with the frequent reminder that in time of war the United States' dependence on foreign ore would be even greater. It was appreciated particularly by the proponents of the Seaway that the development of a supply of foreign ore at competitive prices would greatly lessen the pressure on Lake Superior ore supplies. Thus the Lake Superior reserves would be depleted less rapidly, leaving more ore within the boundaries of the United States for use in the case of a war emergency. Furthermore, prompt supplementing of Lake Superior ore would make possible ore for stockpiling. In 1950 the stock piles were at no more than a very modest level. The major sources or potential sources of iron ore for the United States in 1950 were Canada and Venezuela, with lesser amounts coming from Chile, Brazil and Liberia. Canadian and Venezuelan ore was by far the most accessible of the foreign ores. In both areas there are huge reserves of high-grade ore which can be mined by open-pit methods. Both areas are being developed by the United States iron and steel industry, the Venezuelan ores for use chiefly on the Atlantic Seaboard and the Quebec-Labrador ore for use by Middle Western steel centres. For the steel centres of the Middle West, Quebec-Labrador ore via the Seaway was the cheapest alternative. Venezuelan or other foreign ore via Philadelphia, Baltimore or the St Lawrence would not only have been much more expensive but would have been far more vulnerable during time of war. Venezuelan ores transported to the Atlantic Seaboard would cover a distance in the open ocean of almost 2,000 miles. The Bethlehem Steel Corporation, one of the two large steel producers on the Atlantic Seaboard, lost five of its seven ships transporting ore from Chile to Sparrows Point during the Second World War. The remaining two ships were withdrawn from service. Obviously Venezuelan ore would be equally as vulnerable. It was argued that the Quebec-Labrador ores were much less strategically vulnerable, especially since the Seaway would afford a sheltered route from Seven Islands

into the Great Lakes. Moreover, for the companies concerned in the development of Quebec-Labrador ore nowhere else was the political 'climate' so favourable to the investment of large sums of United States capital. The M. A. Hanna Company of Cleveland and the Hollinger mining interests of Canada were responsible during the 1940s for the exploration of the Quebec-Labrador region, but when an economic deposit had been proven, and that was by 1949, the Iron Ore Company of Canada was formed to build a railway from the concessions to Seven Islands on the St Lawrence, and to mine the ore. The Iron Ore Company of Canada was formed by M. A. Hanna Company and the Hollinger interests, taking in as partners five Middle Western steel companies – Armco, National, Republic, Wheeling, Youngstown Sheet and Tube, as well as the Hanna Coal and Ore Corporation. For the first time in the history of the Seaway battle big business was vitally interested in the Seaway. As an alternative to transportation of Quebec-Labrador ore via the Seaway there was a 1,389-mile open sea route from Seven Islands to Philadelphia or Baltimore, *or* the use of the St Lawrence as far as Montreal, a distance of some 500 miles, and then a rail haul to the steel centres.

It was stated earlier in this chapter that transport costs via the Seaway would be approximately one half the Philadelphia or Baltimore route for ore destined for the Middle Western centres. In 1950 the National Resources Board estimated that, 'assuming normal rail rates, the rates via the port of Philadelphia or Baltimore and by rail thence to Pittsburgh would approximate $3·85 a gross ton. However, via the Seaway transportation costs to Lake Erie ports, Lorain and east, including Cleveland and Buffalo, would approximate only $2·15. Via any other route to these consuming centres the cost of transportation is likely to exceed the cost via the Seaway by at least 75 cents per ton'.

The iron ore argument was as influential in Canada as in the United States. Not only were there those who wanted a good market opened up in the Middle West for Canadian ore, but of course Canada needed the ore as much as the United States, though in lesser quantities. Canada's major steel-producing capacity is in southern Ontario, and these centres use Mesabi iron ore as well as United States Appalachian coal. Thus the Canadian companies are also affected by the diminishing reserves in the Lake Superior fields. Canada, with a market for her own ore, is equally as interested in cheap ore as the Middle Western steel companies.

POWER SHORTAGE

The excellence of the International Rapids section of the St Lawrence River for power development has never been questioned. The first power plant, one with a capacity of 7,500 h.p., was completed at Massena, N.Y., in 1901. Since that time many small and large private companies have sought a licence to develop power on the St Lawrence. In addition both the New York State and the Province of Ontario have been interested in the development. New York first showed a serious interest in the power potential of the St Lawrence by the establishment in 1931 of the Power Authority of the State of New York. A year later the Canadian Government and the province of Ontario agreed that Ontario should be responsible for the development of the International Rapids site. At the same time there was also an agreement to construct the project at the earliest possible time. Unfortunately for upper New York State and Ontario, the Power project now became tied to the Seaway, in United States policy at least, and probably also in Canadian policy. Henceforth neither federal government would allow the development of power alone. But by the end of the Second World War and especially by 1954, the power shortage was so severe that the federal governments might well have been embarrassed into giving New York State and Ontario permission to develop St Lawrence power if they had not decided to proceed with the combined project.

Both Ontario and New York State were faced with the prospect of having to satisfy a rapidly increasing demand for electricity by the installation of additional large coal-burning thermal electric plants. In Ontario in the post-war period thermal plants had had to be installed in Windsor, Hamilton and Toronto. The two plants operated by the Hydro-Electric Power Commission of Ontario at Windsor and Toronto have a total generator capacity of 664,000 kW. Most of the coal used in these plants is imported from the Appalachian fields of the United States; thus it is not cheap coal, and consequently thermal power is expensive, especially when compared to the extremely low average rate for both the domestic and industrial consumer of electricity in Canada as a whole. In 1955 the rate for the domestic consumer averaged 1.66 cents per kWh. in Canada as compared with 2.64 cents in the United States, and commercial and industrial sales averaged 0.7 cents per kWh. in Canada compared with 1.3 cents in the United States.

In the United States in the area considered as a potential market for St Lawrence power, comprising New England less Maine, New York State less a portion of the state to the west of Rochester, the utility systems on 31st December 1951 had a total installed generating capacity of 9,434,000 kW., of which 8,005,000 kW. capacity was in thermal electric plants. As in Ontario, this electricity was expensive. The domestic consumer in New York State was paying approximately 25 per cent more per kWh for electricity than the national average.

In Canada as a whole, in the ten-year period following the Second World War, yearly domestic consumption increased from 3,365 million kWh. to 12,760 million kWh., an increase of over 280 per cent. Not only was this due to an 83 per cent increase in the number of customers being served, but the average consumption for each customer increased by 107 per cent, and in 1955 amounted to 3,500 kWh. Ontario, which contains one-third of the total population of Canada, was obviously responsible for a very large share of this increase. Ontario is also Canada's most industrialised province. Its industries produce almost one half of the nation's manufactured goods. The manufacturing industries demand a tremendous amount of electricity. Two industries alone, the non-ferrous metal smelting and refining industry and the pulp and paper industry, account for over 40 per cent of the power consumed by manufacturers in the province. It is not surprising, then, that by 1954 Ontario Hydro had installed all the readily available power sites up to full capacity, with the exception of the International Rapids section and that was readily available only in the geographical sense. In 1950 Canada and the United States agreed to additional development on the Niagara River, and the Sir Adam Beck Generation Station No. 2 was commenced. The first stage of this development provided much-needed power, especially in Ontario, but the complete development of this site was not due until 1958, so that Ontario not only had to install thermal electric plants but she also had to import power from the province of Quebec, which is much more favourably endowed with hydroelectric potential. Until the thermal plants were installed, afternoon blackouts for domestic consumers of electricity in many of the large southern Ontario towns were common. It is thus obvious that St Lawrence power was a vital necessity to the continued economic development of southern Ontario. Moreover, the nation as a whole would suffer, with Ontario industry working at anything less than full capacity. Ontario Hydro maintains that even with the use of St Lawrence power the province will face a power shortage again in 1962, at the present rate of industrial and residential development. It is to be hoped that by that time nuclear power will be available, the construction of the first Canadian experimental nuclear-electric plant having been started in 1956.

Likewise, New York State needed additional electricity and, if at all possible, at rates lower than the existing rates, which were, as stated earlier, 25 per cent greater than the national average. For some years upper New York State had been importing power from Ontario in the Niagara region, and the Cedar Rapids plant of Quebec Hydro, on the Soulanges section of the St Lawrence River, had been supplying the Alcoa plant at Massena. The addition of a large block of cheaply produced hydroelectric power to the existing systems in New York State would undoubtedly tend to lower rates, and lower rates would increase use. In 1951 the chairman of the Power Authority of New York State, Mr John E. Burton, expressed the sharp discontent of a large section of New York's inhabitants when he said, 'Anyone who takes responsibility for delaying or obstructing the development of the St Lawrence power must also take the responsibility for making the people of New York pay $20,000,000 a year extra for high-priced coal. If the occasion should arise, New York will not hesitate to place responsibility right where it belongs. . . .'

So, New York State in the post-war era was short of power and paying more for it than most other states in the Union. In a 1950 report the United States Federal Power Commission, using as a basis the market area of New England and New York previously described, estimated that the power requirement would practically double in the period 1950–60, and that the required generating capacity in the market area in 1960 would be 13,150,000 kW., compared with the 1951 figure of 9,434,000 kW. Taking into account presently scheduled additions of new generating capacity and the scheduled retirements of existing capacity, it was estimated that the supply of power in 1960 would amount to only 9,605,000 kW. The additional need would thus be 3,545,000 kW. New York's share of the St Lawrence power would be between 700,000 kW. – the dependable capacity – and 940,000 kW. – the full capacity, so that it could undoubtedly be absorbed as soon as it was made available.

In 1952 the United States Federal Power Commission also worked out the comparative minimum annual cost of providing the same amount of capacity and energy from fuel-electric plants as from the St Lawrence project. Their conclusion was as follows: 'It is found that the cost of power from fuel-electric plants would vary depending upon the size of generating units. For the load centres selected, unit sizes range from 160,000 kilowatts down to 20,000 kilowatts. An examination of 1950 fuel costs in the area indicate a range of from 26 cents to 40 cents per million British thermal units with the greater portion of the market area paying about 35 cents per million B.T. units for fuel delivered to plant sites. The estimated minimum cost at the load centres of providing generating capacity from fuel-electric plants equal to the project delivered dependable capacity, and providing energy equal to the project average-year delivered energy, is $40,430,000. If these costs are expressed in terms of energy, the resulting cost per kilowatt-hour of delivered energy would be 6.98 mills.' A mill equals $\frac{1}{10}$ of a United States cent. The corresponding minimum cost of providing St Lawrence capacity and energy would be approximately $24,000,000 and the corresponding delivered costs per average year kilowatt-hour, after allowing for transmission losses, would be 4.29 mills. It is important to remember that the operating cost for a hydroelectric plant remains nearly constant, regardless of energy output. This is not true of a steam plant, which must burn fuel. Consequently every kilowatt-hour generated at the project which eliminates the necessity for a fuel-generated kilowatt-hour has value at least equal to the fuel saved.

The development of a large supply of high-load-factor hydroelectric power in the region of upper New York State also meant that more effective use could be made of the other types of power available in the region. Other hydroelectric developments, both present and future, with the exception of Niagara power, are of the low-load

75

factor, short-peak carrying type. Thus more effective use can be made of the hydro resources of the region by a combination of these two types of projects and their integration with the substantial amount of fuel generation of the region. When this is accomplished with an adequate transmission network for the transfer of power, the flexibility of operation will be increased and greater use can be made of the steam and hydro capacity and energy of the region.

THE DEFENCE ARGUMENT

In the report of the United States Senate Foreign Relations Committee to the 83rd Congress (1954) it was stated that 'The Seaway will constitute an important part of our system of national defence'. The report went on to reiterate the defence arguments for the Seaway, which had been put forward by numerous Congressional committees, Seaway associations, conferences, etc., both in the United States and Canada. Chief of these was the claim that the Seaway would provide access to the reserves of iron ore which would be needed in ever-increasing quantities by the United States and Canadian iron and steel industries in time of war. Not so often pointed out, but equally as important, is the excellent passage which would also be afforded the aluminium production of one of the major producing centres in the world, as well as titanium, another metal of strategic importance. Quite obviously the railroads, particularly from Montreal, south and west, could handle aluminium and titanium ore, but not the tremendous quantities of iron ore, possibly 50 to 60 million tons annually, which would be needed during any future emergency. Questions have been raised concerning the cost of defending the St Lawrence Seaway and its vulnerability as compared with the water route to Philadelphia or Baltimore. It was held that the Seaway project would receive protection against air attack with only slight additional commitment of air defence forces by virtue of the air defence priority already accorded the area, whereas the cost of protecting large numbers of coastal convoys against submarine attack from Labrador to Philadelphia or Baltimore would entail a considerable increase in convoy escort forces. This would be equally true or even more so in the case of Venezuelan ore. Of course, both the power and navigation facilities of the Seaway itself would be vulnerable to air attack, especially by atomic weapons, unless continental defence proves extremely effective, but equally as vulnerable are other mining and transportation facilities in the Great Lakes region, e.g., the Sault Ste Marie canals and ore docks at Lake Erie ports. The proponents of the Seaway claimed that two routes are better than one, and diversity lends strength; the more diverse the economy and the system of communications, the greater can be the war effort.

The Senate Foreign Relations Committee and proponents also claimed that the Seaway would provide access to shipbuilding and ship-repair facilities located in a relatively secure area to supplement coastal shipyards, and that it would furnish an additional needed line of communication for ocean shipping, which can ease wartime strain on rail transportation and the port facilities of the Gulf and Atlantic coasts. The availability of inland ocean-type ports and the inland water route would also make it possible to reduce the length of the ocean journey between Europe and industrial North America by about 1,000 miles.

Finally, in the defence argument it was claimed that the power project would provide large quantities of electricity for defence industries. The aluminium industry was already located at the site of the proposed project so that this argument was quite valid.

THE GENERAL ECONOMIC ARGUMENT

Many proponents of the Seaway and Power projects claimed general economic improvement or industrial expansion as one of the great benefits of the projects. The point has already been made that these claims for general economic improvement seemed somewhat nebulous until large quantities of iron ore were discovered in Quebec-Labrador, but the multitude and great variety of views expressed on the economic outlook and probable impact of the St Lawrence project undoubtedly added weight when the final count of votes was made.

In the final summing up of the economic outlook and impact of the project in the United States and Canada there appeared to be general agreement on the following points:

(1) That the final indebtedness of the Seaway project would be recovered from shipping tolls rather than from general taxation.
(2) That it will assist in the stabilisation of the Middle Western

77

steel industry and associated industries and permit expansion, as contrasted with a shift to the Atlantic Seaboard area.

(3) It will spur further industrialisation in the Great Lakes area and St Lawrence valley which have the advantages of ample water supply, low cost transportation for basic raw materials, and in certain sections cheap hydroelectric power.

(4) It will improve the general economy of the St Lawrence valley and mid-continental area, for reasons already stated, in addition to the benefits accruing from the opening up of the Great Lakes to a greater number of ocean-going freighters and increasing the distance that the present 'lakers' can travel downstream. The grain trade is particularly likely to benefit.

(5) It will increase integration of the United States and Canadian economies with benefits accruing to both countries.

(6) The Seaway will produce some unavoidable dislocation, mostly of short-term effect. The same may be said of any material progress, such as the coming of canals, railroads, highways, pipelines and aeroplanes. In every case, after a period of adjustment, further gains have accrued to all elements of the economy.

The first two points have already been discussed at sufficient length. The other claims bear further examination.

Prior to the decision on the part of the United States and Canada to construct the Seaway and Power projects it was impossible to forecast with any accuracy the extent to which industry and the general economy would expand as a result of the projects. The importance of water transport, both lake-type and ocean-type, in a region comprising the densely settled sections of two major Canadian provinces, Quebec and Ontario, and eight states of the United States, is obviously incalculable. The area contains the heart of the North American manufacturing belt, the greatest industrial concentration in the world, with possibly the largest steel-making capacity in existence. The population is approximately 70 million or about 40 per cent of the United States population and 60 per cent of the Canadian population. Almost every major industry is represented and a tremendous variety of raw materials are processed in the region. Many of these raw materials, agricultural, forest and mineral, are found within the immediate hinterland, but the majority have to be transported considerable distances within the Great Lakes–St Lawrence region.

UNITED STATES DEPARTMENT OF COMMERCE ESTIMATE OF POTENTIAL TRAFFIC 1949

Commodity	Potential traffic
Iron ore	30 to 37½ million tons
Grain	6½ to 11½ million tons
Coal	4 million tons
Petroleum	6 to 20 million tons
Agricultural machinery	48,000 tons
Automobiles, parts, and accessories	640,000 tons
Iron and steel	1,371,000 tons
Office appliances and parts	7,000 tons
Wheat flour	555,000 tons
Industrial chemicals	13,000 tons
Coffee	245,000 tons
Sugar	963,000 tons
Oil seeds	125,000 tons
Wool, unmanufactured	6,000 tons
Newsprint paper	121,000 tons
Manganese, chrome, and ferro alloy ores and metals, n. e. s.	240,000 tons
Copper, refined and unrefined	34,000 tons
Nitrogenous fertilizer materials	25,000 tons
Residual general cargo traffic	6,885,000 tons
Ballast shipping	25½ to 42 million dead-weight tons

Various estimates suggest that savings as high as 50 per cent in transport costs for some commodities will result from the Seaway. Until the final toll charge schedule is announced no verdict on these pre-Seaway claims is possible. The transport of bulk products, iron ore, grain, coal, petroleum, iron and steel, and sugar will dominate Seaway traffic, and as this traffic will largely be in the form of lakers and tankers considerable economies should result from the extension of the deep waterway. Many estimates have been made of the benefits of the Seaway to the grain trade. The most reliable of these suggest considerable savings in the cost of marketing grain. One Canadian official stated that 'If large lakers can carry wheat the whole 1,200 miles to Montreal (rather than to Prescott, Ontario) the total water freight would not be more than 11 cents a bushel instead of the present 16 cents, not counting the saving in transhipment charges of not less than another cent a bushel. But the savings promise to be even greater than that, thanks to the upbound movement of iron ore in sight. Carriers delivering ore from Sept Isles to Lake Erie ports would find it of advantage to pick up grain delivered to Port Colborne (on the Lake Erie shore of Ontario), or, better still, they could proceed to the Lakehead to pick up grain for Montreal or beyond. Since upbound cargoes promise to outweigh the downbound – just the opposite of today – competition for these downbound cargoes should lower the rates and give western farmers the greater part of the benefit from the additional economy'. The initial claim was probably much more realistic than the latter. With the short navigation season there will be considerable pressure on the existing shipping to turn around as rapidly as possible so that there is very little likelihood of iron ore carriers becoming involved in the grain trade. An American expert claimed that transport charges via the Seaway route will probably be 15 cents to 20 cents per bushel less than the charges over the existing routes to the Atlantic ports. He does point out, however, that future competitive rate-cutting might reduce this saving to 10 cents a bushel.

And what of the claim that there will be a tremendous increase in overseas trade, that the Great Lakes will become a second 'Mediterranean', with major ports equal to the existing great ports of the world? Most of the arguments on this point appear to have centred on the estimates of the proportion of the world's shipping able to navigate the 27-foot channel. These estimates varied considerably, some being as high as 75 per cent of the world's shipping, but, as one opponent of the Seaway claimed, this percentage included a large number of Chinese junks which are not likely to sail far from the shores of China. What seemed to be more important was not the number of ships available for the overseas trade but the nature and the size of that trade, because, as proponents claimed, where there's trade there will be shipping. If the toll structure is not too formidable

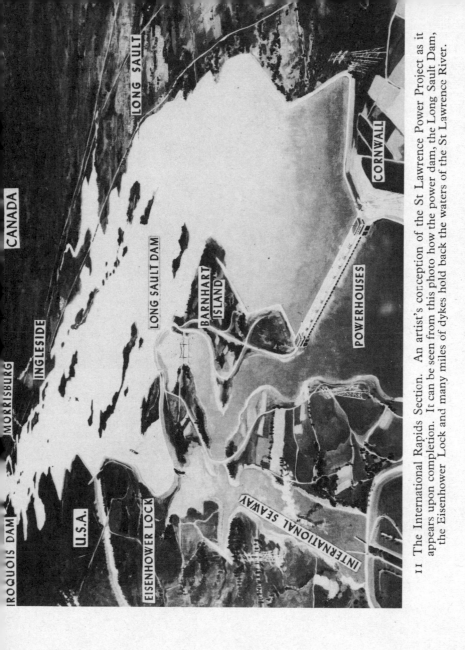

MORRISBURG · CANADA

IROQUOIS DAM

INGLESIDE

LONG SAULT

U.S.A.

LONG SAULT DAM

BARNHART ISLAND

EISENHOWER LOCK

POWERHOUSES

CORNWALL

INTERNATIONAL SEAWAY

11 The International Rapids Section. An artist's conception of the St Lawrence Power Project as it appears upon completion. It can be seen from this photo how the power dam, the Long Sault Dam, the Eisenhower Lock and many miles of dykes hold back the waters of the St Lawrence River.

The St Lawrence Power Project.

12 *Above:* An aerial view of the joint powerhouses of the Ontario Hydro Commission and the Power Authority of the state of New York. The overall length is 3,300 feet, with a maximum height of 162 feet above the foundations. The 32 units have a maximum capacity of 1,880,000 kilowatts.

13 *Below:* Construction under way during the winter of 1957.

and the tariff builders do not have their way, then overseas trade should expand very rapidly.

The Great Lakes overseas trade was pioneered in 1933 by a Norwegian shipping line. The trade did not expand very rapidly and was discontinued during the Second World War, but the trade was re-established in 1945 and has since expanded at a phenomenal rate. By 1954 14 shipping lines and 120 vessels were involved, exactly double the number in 1952. In 1946 a total of 23 vessels left the port of Chicago for European ports, but by 1954 the number of vessels sailing out of Chicago had increased to 225.

In 1953 the total combined imports and exports of the United States and Canada amounted to approximately $24 billion. Of this amount approximately $10 billion represented trade with Europe, and the shortest and cheapest route from the heart of the North American manufacturing belt is the Great Lakes–St Lawrence route. With considerable expansion of industrial production anticipated, and continued agricultural production, shipping in ever-increasing tonnage will find its way into the upper St Lawrence and the Great Lakes.

Whilst the increase in overseas trade will contribute a great deal to the success of the Seaway, it is the lake shipping which will undoubtedly benefit the most. In fact the term 'lakeway' is being used frequently rather than 'seaway'. In the final report of the United States Senate Foreign Relations Committee it was stated that '75 per cent of the traffic will be transported in lake-type vessels which can be satisfactorily handled by the 27-foot channel, thus only 25 per cent of the traffic is subject to movement in seagoing ships'. Lakers will carry ore from Seven Islands to the ore ports of the Great Lakes as they will continue to do from Lake Superior. Grain will be carried by lakers at least as far as Montreal.

AN ALL-CANADIAN SEAWAY

In the final stages of the Seaway battle no more convincing argument was necessary than that Canada would build the Seaway herself. It was in 1949 that the Prime Minister of Canada first suggested that Canada might be forced to develop the power phase alone if the United States would not agree to the combined project. In 1950 Lester Pearson, then Secretary of State for External Affairs, also expressed these sentiments and went a little farther, 'Canadians want to see the St Lawrence development begin in 1951. We are anxious for early ratification of the agreement which our two countries signed in 1941. If that cannot be obtained, however, we shall have to consider the plan put forward by New York State and the Province of Ontario for development of the power alone. If that plan were to be adopted it might also be advisable for Canada to look into the possibility of building at the same time a Canadian deep waterway on our side of the border.'

At a White House conference in September 1951 the Canadian Prime Minister gave the final warning that Canada was willing to proceed with an 'All-Canadian' project if joint development were not possible. Three months later the Canadian Parliament authorised the establishment of the St Lawrence Seaway Authority to co-operate with the United States in construction of navigation facilities in the International Rapids section. Canada was obviously still hopeful that the 1941 agreement would be approved early in the 1952 session of Congress. Although it was another two years before that approval was obtained, the Canadian decision to 'go it alone' must have been responsible for reversing the vote of a number of United States Representatives and Senators. The Senate Foreign Relations Committee in their final report to the Senate stated that 'Perhaps there is no more telling argument in favour of the project than that Canada has decided to build a Seaway with or without the United States. Canada has completed substantial improvements and has now determined to go ahead with an all-Canadian route if the United States does not participate, conditioned only on the power phase being placed under construction. Since the Seaway is a joint interest of both the United States and Canada, the committee is convinced that the United States should join Canada in promptly completing the Seaway. Thus in assuming an equitable share of the costs of construction we shall have an equitable share in its operation and administration – a voice in determining tolls, commodity by commodity, roles of measurement, amount of tolls after the payoff period, etc. Since by far the dominant portion of the traffic will either originate or terminate in the United States, it is obvious that business interests in our country are vitally concerned, as demonstrated by tolls discussion on the Panama Canal.'

Power Projects – The Idea

President Truman before Congress in 1952 expressed the same sentiments when he stated, 'The question before the Congress, therefore, no longer is whether the St Lawrence Seaway should be built. The question before the Congress now is whether the United States shall participate in its construction, and thus maintain joint operation and control over this development which is so important to our security and our economic progress. I strongly believe that the United States should join as a full partner with Canada in building the Seaway. We should not be content to be merely a customer of Canada's for the use of the Seaway after it is built.'

The first Canadian Seaway legislation went into the books in December 1951. The St Lawrence Seaway Authority was established at that time. In the same year Canada had decided on a new approach to the Power project. The Canadian Government decided to attempt to use the machinery provided by the Boundary Waters Treaty of 1909 and to persuade the United States Government to join with Canada in supporting concurrent applications to the International Joint Commission by the Hydro-Electric Power Commission of Ontario and the Power Authority of the State of New York for the development of the power potentialities in the International Rapids section.

Early in 1952 a joint application was made by Canada and the United States to the International Joint Commission for the construction of the power phase of the project. These concurrent applications contemplated the construction of the power and navigation works between Montreal and Lake Erie. In October 1952 the International Joint Commission issued an Order of Approval authorising the joint construction of works for the development of the St Lawrence power. Hence it was that it took more than thirty years before a decision to proceed was rendered, and then not until Canada found it necessary to revert to the 1909 Boundary Waters Treaty.

It has already been made clear that the proponents of the Seaway and Power projects in Canada shared many of the United States arguments for the projects. It must be kept in mind that many of these arguments were of long standing in Canada, and the earlier St Lawrence canals were built entirely by Canada for a variety of economic reasons.

If there was caution shown by Canada or any group of Canadians during early Seaway proceedings it was because of the relative failure of the early canals. In consideration of the small population in Canada compared to the United States the earlier canals had been very costly. The cost of any future improvements in relation to total Canadian resources would undoubtedly be less, but a considerable section of the Canadian population felt for a long time that Canadians should no longer be burdened with the complete cost of the navigation facilities on the St Lawrence and the Niagara Peninsula, which were available free-of-charge to United States shipping.

It has already been stated that there was no distinct opposition lobby in Canada as there was in the United States. Opposition both to the Seaway and the Power projects rose from time to time but it was never well organised. Prior to the 1932 St Lawrence power agreement between the Canadian Government and the province of Ontario there was considerable opposition to the suggestion that the Federal government might develop the St Lawrence power potential. There was for a time opposition to the Seaway project by Montreal and other ports on the lower St Lawrence, which feared that their port function would suffer as the result of deep navigation being provided into the Great Lakes.

The port function of Quebec had declined with each deepening of the St Lawrence upstream to Montreal. Why not Montreal? Toronto and other ports on Lake Ontario claimed that they would in fact develop at Montreal's expense. Convincing arguments were later provided by Seaway proponents that Montreal and most of the ports on the St Lawrence and Lake Ontario would undoubtedly gain as a result of an increase in commerce on the inland waterway.

Though it was frequently claimed by some opponents that Canadian railroads would face a decline in traffic with the construction of the Seaway, there was never any convincing argument produced to that effect. The Canadian railroads are largely complementary to domestic shipping on the St Lawrence and the Great Lakes. The railroads feed grain to the ports on Lake Superior, distribute grain for domestic use within south-eastern Canada and take over the movement of grain in winter, particularly from Great Lakes and St Lawrence elevations to the Atlantic ports.

The forecasted traffic on the future Seaway would largely comprise increased quantities of the bulk commodities handled on the existing canal system so that competition was not likely to develop. Rather would the railroads benefit with an increase in commerce as a result of the Seaway and Power projects.

When finally Seaway and Power development legislation was placed before the Canadian Houses of Parliament there was little effective opposition. Canadians for a long time had shown a lack of enthusiasm rather than effective opposition to the combined project.

THE SWING BEGINS

It is difficult to say just when the proponents of the Seaway and Power projects began to win their battle in the United States Congress. In the House of Representatives the House Committee on Public Works was responsible for the Seaway resolution, but it was not until 22nd February 1954 that it ever emerged from the committee stage. In the Senate it was 12th January 1954 before debate of the resolution of the Senate Committee on Foreign Relations began in the Senate.

In the Senate in post-war years the fight against the Seaway had been led by Senator Lodge of Massachusetts, representing eastern railroads, the port of Boston and the New England Council, and by Senator Connolly of Texas, long a Seaway opponent, on behalf of Texas railroads and Texas Gulf ports. Senator Lodge led the fight on the Senate floor, while Senator Connolly, as Chairman of the Foreign Relations Committee, fought it in committee, and there, as we have seen, it stayed for a long time. Others who made up the hard core of opposition included, for example, Senator Kilgore of West Virginia, whose vote for the Power project would have meant his political death as the representative of a coalmining population. Senator Tydings of Maryland, who was chairman of one of Senator Connolly's sub-committees, did an excellent job of blocking Seaway legislation on behalf of the Port of Baltimore. Senator Smith of New Jersey and Senator Ives of New York likewise fought the Seaway on behalf of New York interests. Senator Robert Taft of Ohio also vigorously opposed the project during the Democratic term of office, but he was one of the first to reverse his vote to support the Seaway proposals of the Republican Eisenhower administration in 1952.

Meanwhile, outside Congress the opposition began to buckle, though slowly. The first of the really strong industrial opponents to go was the Pittsburgh Consolidation Coal Company. It was lined up to support the Seaway means of cheap transport for Quebec-Labrador ore. The defection of a major coal company gradually broke the ranks of a strong element of the A.A.R. Other industries, especially those associated with the Middle Western steel industries, began to waver. The automobile industry began by giving at least token assistance to the Seaway lobby. Many of Eisenhower's cabinet also began to defect to the Seaway cause and along with them went many major industrial interests. Charles Wilson, president of General Electric, who had previously opposed the Seaway and Power projects very firmly, now came out in favour of it. George Humphrey of the M. A. Hanna Company, who also at one time opposed the Seaway, now as Secretary of the United States Treasury helped to organise the battle for approval. By 1953 opposition in the Senate had also begun to crumble. Mention has already been made of Senator Taft's reversal. Senator John Kennedy of Massachusetts became the first Senator from that state to vote for the Seaway in twenty years. Senator Symington of Missouri also reversed that state's traditional opposition. Amongst the men who finally led the way to victory were Representatives Dondero and Senator Wiley of Wisconsin. The Seaway and Power projects 'enabling' legislation carried their names. The Wiley-Dondero Act became law on 13th May 1954.

However, there was a dying fling on the part of Seaway and Power opponents. Both the Central Pennsylvania Coal Producers' Association and the Lake Ontario Land Development and Beach Protection Association had, prior to the enactment of the Wiley-Dondero legislation, appealed to the United States Court of Appeals against the decision of Federal Power Commission to grant a licence to the New York State Power Authority to develop the American share of the St Lawrence power. The request for a rehearing of the case was denied, but an appeal was later made to the United States Supreme Court for a review of the decision, but this was also denied. And so died the opposition! But opponents have a way of being vindictive (see Chapter 5, p. 150).

CHAPTER FOUR

The St Lawrence Seaway and Power Projects – The Creation

THE CREATION

The past chapter has shown that the St Lawrence Seaway and Power projects started one of the strongest lobbies and gave rise to what was probably one of the longest political battles in United States history. There have been few single projects over which the United States and Canada have consulted so often and for so long. The project also ranks with the greatest engineering undertakings of all time. Such a project would have so ranked if it had been undertaken in a remote and sparsely populated area, but its claim to greatness is even more justified when it is appreciated that the zone of construction was one of the most densely populated and most continuously built-up areas in North America. Administrative and engineering problems were thus extremely complex.

In the design and construction of the complete project there were eleven major authorities and numerous minor authorities involved. Practically all the major authorities and a lesser number of minor ones had to be consulted and agreement had to be reached before construction on any phase of the project could be commenced. A consideration of the function of these major authorities is necessary before proceeding with a detailed description of the design and construction of the project.

It goes without saying that the Canadian Parliament and the United States Congress were the supreme authorities in this international project. They were responsible for enacting the legislation which created the authorities most directly responsible for the construction of the navigation facilities, and by agreement with the province of Ontario and the Legislature of the State of New York the power-constructing entities were created. The Federal Governments were also responsible for organising the administration of each of the authorities and for making the appointments to top administrative posts. They were responsible for the financing of loans which are due to be repaid over a period of fifty years. Each authority was also granted powers of expropriation by the respective Federal Government.

The International Joint Commission, which comprises three members from Canada and three from the United States, is responsible for all matters concerning the boundary waters between Canada and the United States. This Commission was established by the Boundary Waters Treaty of 1909, and it has been concerned ever since with all the Seaway and Power deliberations. It was the medium through which the Seaway and Power projects were launched. The Commission has had to approve all plans for both projects.

Under the order approving the power works, the governments of Canada and the United States agreed to establish the Joint Board of Engineers, to be known as the St Lawrence River Joint Board of Engineers. This Board consists of an equal number of representatives from both countries. The duties of the Joint Board of Engineers were to review, co-ordinate and approve the plans and the programme of construction. The duties and responsibilities of the Joint Board related to the construction phase of the power development alone, and involved the approval, prior to construction, and supervision during construction, of all the works proposed to be constructed by either the Hydro-Electric Power Commission of Ontario in Canada, or the Power Authority of the State of New York in the United States.

The International Joint Commission's Order of Approval provided for the appointment of a Board of Control, to be known as the International St Lawrence River Board of Control. The duties of that Board related to water levels and the regulation of the discharge of water from Lake Ontario and the flow of water through the International Rapids section. The reason for the appointment of this Board was that the power works would radically change the regimen of the St Lawrence River for a distance of 50 miles. The power works, for example, included extensive channel enlargements, which involved the removal of the natural river control of the Galop Rapids and the substitution of an artificial control at Iroquois Point. The responsibility of the Board of Control was intended to be advisory and exploratory in character and related to the devising of both temporary and permanent methods of regulating the outflows of Lake Ontario and the flow through the International Rapids section. The functions of this Board will extend beyond the construction period, and will involve the administration of a method or methods of control approved by the governments of Canada and the United States upon the recommendation of the International Joint Commission.

The International Lake Ontario Board of Engineers was appointed by the International Joint Commission to investigate complaints made by residents of the south shore of Lake Ontario, because of the damage occasioned by the extremely high water levels of 1951 and 1952. The levels reached a height unencountered since 1870. The outcome of the investigation was an order provided by the International Joint Commission requiring levels on Lake Ontario to be kept as nearly as possible within a range of 244 to 248 feet during the navigation season.

In Canada the provincial authorities involved are the provinces of Ontario and Quebec. The province of Ontario is involved by virtue of the fact that a provincial agency, the Hydro-Electric Power Commission of Ontario, is the entity designated by Canada to construct the power works in the International Rapids section. Both operations also involve provincial territory and population. The Province of Quebec was interested in the power and navigation works chiefly because these works altered the natural regimen of the river and necessitated the regulation of Lake Ontario by artificial means, which could have either a beneficial or an injurious effect upon the interests of that province downstream. New York State was involved because the Power Authority it established in 1930 was the entity designated by the United States Government to join with the Hydro Commission of Ontario for the development of power. The nature of the power works is such that co-ordinated effort by the two power entities was absolutely essential.

Finally, there were the two major authorities involved in the Seaway project: the St Lawrence Seaway Authority of Canada and the St Lawrence Seaway Development Corporation of the United States. In the following discussion emphasis will be placed in the early phases upon the Seaway project and later upon the Power project and associated relocation and rehabilitation projects.

The St Lawrence Seaway

The St Lawrence Seaway Authority Act of 1951 created the St Lawrence Seaway Authority for the purposes of (a) acquiring lands for and constructing, maintaining and operating any such works as may be necessary to provide and maintain, either wholly in Canada, or in conjunction with works undertaken by an appropriate authority in the United States, a deep waterway between the port of Montreal and Lake Erie; and (b) constructing, maintaining and operating all such works in connection with such a deep waterway as the Governor in Council may deem necessary to fulfil any obligations undertaken or to be undertaken by Canada pursuant to any present or future agreement. The Act further interprets 'deep waterway' as meaning 'adequate provision for navigation requiring a controlling channel depth of twenty-seven feet with a depth of thirty feet over lock sills'. Clause 13 of the Act enables the Authority, 'from time to time, to borrow money from His Majesty or otherwise for the purposes for which it is incorporated'.

The Wiley-Dondero Act of 1954 provided for creation of the St Lawrence Seaway Development Corporation 'to construct part of the St Lawrence Seaway in United States Territory in the interest of national security; authorizing the Corporation to summate certain arrangements with the St Lawrence Seaway Authority of Canada relative to construction and operation of the Seaway; empowering the Corporation to finance the United States share of the Seaway cost on a self-liquidating basis; to establish co-operation with Canada in the control and operation of the St Lawrence Seaway'. More specifically, the Corporation was authorised and directed to construct in United States territory deepwater navigation works, with a controlling depth of 27 feet in channels and canals and with locks at least 800 feet long, 80 feet wide, and 30 feet over the sills. The Corporation was also required to make necessary arrangements to assure the co-ordination of its activities with those of its Canadian counterpart.

WORK COMMENCES

With purpose clearly defined, authority and money appropriated, the St Lawrence Seaway Authority of Canada and the St Lawrence Seaway Development Corporation of the United States commenced work at several points on the St Lawrence River in the autumn of 1954.

Power Projects – The Creation

In a period of approximately four and a half years the Seaway was completed. It took ten years to construct the Suez Canal, twenty-four years for the Panama Canal and thirty years for the first St Lawrence Canal system. It may be argued that the economic significance of the Seaway has been greatly exaggerated, but it would be difficult to exaggerate the magnitude and complexity of the task which faced particularly the Canadian Seaway authority. The completion of every phase of construction and remedial work on time, and frequently well ahead of schedule, not only reflects creditably upon Canadian and United States engineering skill, but it also indicates the degree of success met by the respective Seaway authorities in co-operating with private, national, state and provincial authorities as well as the successful co-operation of the United States and Canadian Seaway authorities themselves.

The major objective, that of the construction of a deep waterway between Montreal and Lake Erie, involved the Canadian Authority in a multitude of projects hardly envisaged by the original proponents of the scheme. The organisation of a vast administrative machine under the control of the President of the Authority was not the least of these. Included was a public relations and information section which did a magnificent job in educating many millions of Canadians, Americans and overseas visitors in the nature of the Seaway.

For the Seaway engineers there was the carrying out of field surveys, including sub-surface investigations, metering of river flow, sounding of lakes and river channels; the construction and testing of hydraulic lock and river models; the actual designing and construction of navigation facilities, including canals, locks, to mention but a few of their tasks. Very close co-operation was required with all groups affected by the development, particularly with reference to remedial works which included the shifting of towns and the development of new town sites, the landscaping of extensive areas adjacent to the Seaway, railway and highway relocation and the construction of new bridges and lift spans.

A JOURNEY ON THE SEAWAY

In order to gain a clear impression of what has been constructed and of the country through which the Seaway passes we will take an imaginary journey up the St Lawrence and through the Great Lakes to Fort William, one of the great grain ports on Lake Superior. Imagine yourself aboard an 8,000-ton passenger-carrying freighter proceeding from the lower St Lawrence to the upper Great Lakes. This vessel, by the way, is at least four times heavier than the largest vessels using the old canal system. You will be in an excellent position to observe not only the navigational facilities but also the hydro-electric power development on the St Lawrence, the new towns, the recreational areas and the industrial expansion resulting from the Seaway and Power development.

From the Atlantic Ocean to Montreal a deep-water ship channel, known officially as the St Lawrence Ship Channel, is available for navigation. A minimum depth of 35 feet is maintained even at low water, but at various points between Quebec and Montreal dredging is necessary to maintain this minimum. This depth of channel allows ships of up to 25,000 tons to berth in the harbour of Montreal. This section of our journey takes us approximately fifteen hours, but if the journey is made in daylight these fifteen hours will go quickly by because this section of the St Lawrence takes us through one of the most beautiful landscapes on the continent of North America. Nowhere else in the world can a large ocean-going vessel travel so far into the heart of a continent and provide the passenger with such a variety of scenery. For most of the journey intensively farmed fields sweep back in narrow lots from the banks of the river, with this pattern broken only by attractive farm cottages and villages clustered around church spires shining in the sun. Early in the day the city of Quebec suddenly rises picturesquely out of the valley, appearing like some giant fortress yet with an old-world beauty that is unique in North America. Seven miles west of Quebec the Quebec Bridge, a magnificent cantilever structure, spans a gorge-like section of the St Lawrence. Halfway to Montreal mountainous piles of pulp logs signal our approach to Trois Rivieres, one of the great pulp and paper centres of the province. Several hours later the sight of Mount Royal rising out of the lowland ahead heralds our arrival within the outskirts of Greater Montreal. The Jacques Cartier Bridge, the main road link between Montreal and its southshore communities, appears to frame the centre of Montreal, set as it is on the lower slopes of Mount Royal.

The first feature of the Seaway proper is a turning basin at the entrance to an $18\frac{1}{2}$-mile-long canal which takes us around the southern edge of the Laprairie Basin, then overland to Lake St Louis. This route allows for a complete bypass of the Lachine Rapids and a total lift of 45 feet. From the turning basin at the entrance to the Seaway our ship passes under the central span of the southern half of the Jacques Cartier Bridge, which now provides a clearance of 120 feet. All the spans of this section of the bridge had to be raised varying heights to allow for a maximum lift of 50 feet at the centre, to provide the regulation 120 feet clearance. The raising of this bridge was one of the outstanding engineering feats of the Seaway project. The details of this story will be told later. Allowing for a speed of 10 to 12 m.p.h. in the canal and thirty minutes in each lock, it will take about three hours to reach Lake St Louis. In the old Lachine Canal it took up to ten hours to cover the same distance.

We now find ourselves in the canal proper. The channel is only 27 feet deep, but this is, of course, a very great improvement over the 14 feet of the old Lachine Canal. The width of the canal at this point is 225 feet. The maximum size of vessel allowed in the Seaway will be one with a length of 730 feet and a beam of 75 feet, so that with a canal width of 225 feet there is certainly sufficient room for two-way traffic. A dyke with a top width of 40 feet and a height of 30 feet above the water of the canal separates the canal from the river. These solidly constructed dykes are necessary to protect the canal from the flow of the St Lawrence in winter and summer and from the action of ice in winter. In normal operation the canal water level will be a few feet higher than the river, but under winter ice conditions the river level occasionally rises to heights of 20 feet or more above the canal water level. Above the Côte Ste Catherine Lock the dykes are much thicker than the average because they have a maximum head of water of about 40 feet against them. The pressure of ice in the Laprairie Basin is tremendous. Under natural conditions ice was often piled into great ridges around the edge of the basin. It actually would be possible under exceptionally severe winter conditions even now for ice ridges to burst over the dykes.

To the left, that is on the south side of the canal, there is an extensive reclaimed area which is to be used for recreational purposes as well as for the improvement of highway facilities along the south shore. These amenities will partly compensate communities for the loss of a very attractive riverfront.

LENGTH AND LIMITING DIMENSIONS OF GREAT LAKES–ST LAWRENCE NAVIGATION CHANNEL BEFORE AND AFTER CONSTRUCTION

CHANNEL	LENGTH (miles)	DEPTH Pre-Seaway Upbound (feet)	DEPTH Pre-Seaway Downbound (feet)	DEPTH Seaway (feet)	NUMBER OF LOCKS Pre-Seaway	NUMBER OF LOCKS Seaway	PRE-SEAWAY Lock Size (feet)
St Mary's River	63	21	25	0	0	0	—
MacArthur Lock at Sault Ste Marie	0	31	31	0	1	0	800 × 80 × 31
Straits of Mackinac	20	27	27	0	0	0	—
St Clair and Detroit Rivers	88	21	25	0	0	0	—
Welland Canal	28	25	25	27	8	0	800 × 80 × 30
St Lawrence River:							
Thousand Islands	68	27	27	27	0	0	
International Rapids	46	14	14	27	12	3	252 × 44 × 14
Canadian Section	68	14	14	27	10	4	252 × 44 × 14
Montreal to Sea	1,000	35	35	0	0	0	—

Power Projects – The Creation

Immediately downstream from the St Lambert Lock the canal widens. This widening has been made in anticipation of the need for a twin lock in the years to come. The excavation has been completed, but no other facilities have been constructed as yet.

Two miles from the entrance to the Seaway we enter the St Lambert Lock, which raises our vessel the necessary 15 feet from the level of Montreal Harbour (22 feet above sea level) to the level of Laprairie Basin. This lock has the same general dimensions of all the Seaway locks and these are patterned on the dimensions of the Welland Canal. The usable length of the lock is 768 feet, the width is 80 feet and the depth over the sills 30 feet. Approaching any one of these locks the first noticeable piece of lock machinery is the wire-rope fender stretched across the entrance. In the event of a ship losing control on approaching the lock the ship would first strike the fender boom and not the lock gates. Each of the fenders can absorb in a distance of 70 feet the impact of a ship almost twice the dead-weight tonnage of the largest ship likely to travel the Seaway. On the approach to the lock shipping is controlled by a system of red and green lights which are located on the approach walls just ahead of the fenders. Once the signal to enter the lock is given the fenders are raised and the ship sails into the lock. The lock gates are automatically controlled to begin swinging open rather slowly at first, to speed up, and then to slow down again before stopping. As the gates close again water begins to flow rapidly into the lock.

Although the average lift at the St Lambert Lock is 15 feet, the actual lift will vary from 23 feet to 5 feet depending on the water level of Montreal Harbour. Obviously if less movement of water is necessary, passage through the lock will be faster. The average time will be thirty minutes.

As our ship passes into the lock it also passes under a lift span in the Victoria Bridge, the property of the Canadian National Railway. The Victoria Bridge, a combined road and rail bridge, was initially constructed in 1860 and rebuilt in 1898. Modification of this bridge to enable continuous traffic to flow while ships are passing through the canal and locks provided one of the biggest headaches of the whole Seaway project. A solution was found to this problem by providing another bridge, with lift span, immediately upstream from the upstream lock-gate. By using the canal banks and specially

95

constructed embankments, traffic is kept flowing. As we pass under the downstream lift span, all the traffic has been diverted to the upstream bridge, which also carries both road and rail traffic – in this case one above the other. Once our ship passes through the lock all the traffic is diverted back to the main Victoria Bridge.

Beyond the St Lambert Lock the canal extends in an unbroken stretch for 8 miles around the Laprairie Basin. Soon after entering this section we pass the foundation piers of what is supposed to become by 1961 the Champlain Bridge, the third bridge across Montreal Harbour between the Island of Montreal and the south shore of the St Lawrence. The Champlain Bridge will carry motor traffic only. Within the Laprairie channel there are two turning basins to allow ships to manœuvre in and out of this section of the Seaway. On the south side of the channel an extensive area has been reclaimed and set aside for industrial development. Berthage facilities have consequently been provided for several miles along the south side of the channel and within the turning basins.

The Laprairie Basin channel leads us to the Côte Ste Catherine Lock, which will provide a lift of between 30 and 40 feet depending upon the difference in level of Lake St Louis and the water of the Laprairie Basin channel.

An overland channel has been provided for the next 2 miles to bypass the Lachine Rapids. The channel has its outlet in Lake St Louis. But before the upstream outlet is reached two bridges are passed. The first is the Honore Mercier Bridge which carries motor traffic above the Lachine Rapids from Ville Lasalle on the Island of Montreal to Caughnawaga on the south shore. New southern approaches had to be constructed to provide the necessary clearance of 120 feet. In the construction of the Honore Mercier Bridge allowance had been made for future Seaway traffic, but unfortunately this allowance was made on the north side of the river. The bridge had a descending ramp at its southern end where the Seaway channel passes through, so that this had to be destroyed and replaced by a high-level crossing over the Seaway. The opportunity was taken of greatly improving the southern approaches to the bridge, and the western approach has been maintained at a high level for a considerable distance to allow traffic to pass over the Canadian Pacific Railway embankment and to bypass the Indian village of Caughnawaga, which has for many years been a terrible bottleneck, particularly for Sunday-afternoon traffic. This development is an excellent example of how the Seaway development has resulted in a great improvement in motor traffic facilities across the St Lawrence. Immediately beyond the Honore Mercier Bridge the double-track main line of the Canadian Pacific Railway now crosses the canal on two new single-track lift bridges.

At this point we enter Lake St Louis and are opposite the entrance to the old Lachine Canal. We have now been in the Seaway for nearly three hours. In this short time we have overcome an obstacle which kept deep-draught ocean-shipping out of the upper St Lawrence and Great Lakes for close on two centuries. At least half of the channel across Lake St Louis had to be dredged and in places solid rock had to be removed to provide a channel depth of 27 feet. Dredges will need to work in this channel from time to time to maintain this required depth. The channel is clearly marked across the lake by means of brightly coloured buoys.

SOULANGES SECTION

The 18-mile-long Soulanges Section extends from the head of Lake St Louis to the foot of Lake St Francis. In this distance there is an average fall of 82 feet. Two locks and the Beauharnois Power Canal provide a bypass of the Cascades, Split Rock, Cedar and Coteau rapids, as well as the power installations at the downstream end of the Power canal. The Beauharnois Power Development currently utilises the 82-foot head of water at this site for the development of 1,408,000 h.p., an amount which will ultimately be increased to two million h.p. The Beauharnois Power Canal was built originally to serve three purposes. Obviously its chief function has been to carry the greater part of the flow of the St Lawrence River, but at the same time it had to act as a reservoir in which a definite level of water could be maintained. This level is largely maintained by a series of control dams across the main channel of the St Lawrence, the flow of which is also utilised for the development of power. There is a much smaller power-house below the Cedar Rapids. Because the Power canal also had to act as a reservoir, its dimensions are considerable. It is 16 miles in length, 27 feet deep, and is flanked by embankments about 3,300 feet apart. Its third function was to serve as a navigational canal, if, and when, the 27-foot Seaway plan should become a reality. It is interesting to reflect that the idea of a 27-foot Seaway was first proposed soon after the turn of the century, that the Beauharnois Power Canal was constructed in 1928, and the Seaway finally undertaken and completed between 1954 and 1959. During the construction of the Beauharnois Power Canal allowance was made in the structure of the two combined highway and railway bridges for the future installation of vertical lift spans to provide the regulation, clear horizontal width of 200 feet and the vertical clearance of 120 feet. This foresight saved the Seaway engineers additional bridge modification.

In the construction of the lower Beauharnois locks allowance had to be made for highway traffic which circumvents the Beauharnois Power installations at the downstream end. To ensure uninterrupted traffic, a four-lane tunnel has been constructed under the lower lock.

The approach to the Beauharnois locks is most spectacular. To our right the St Lawrence tumbles over the Cascades Rapids to merge with the waters of the Ottawa River and together flow into Lake St Louis. On our left the tremendous structure of the Beauharnois power-house towers above us. This power-house, one of the largest in the world, does not have the impressive location of the Hoover or Grand Coulee dams, but from the level of Lake St Louis its length of more than a half of a mile provides a massive spectacle which is often not appreciated by the passing motorist. It takes a ship over an hour to traverse the two locks and another hour and a quarter to navigate the Power Canal to Lake St Francis. Ahead of us is a 29-mile-long journey across the centre of Lake St Francis. A major programme of dredging was here necessary to provide the 27-foot channel, and in the future dredges will periodically have to maintain sections of this channel.

The shores of Lake St Francis are fringed by trees and cottages, but, immediately beyond, farmland extends back to higher land. To the south the surface rises gradually to the Adirondack Mountains of New York, which on a clear day certainly tower their full 5,000 feet above the lowlands. To the north the farmlands of Quebec and then Ontario fringe higher outliers of the Canadian Shield. In summer this extensive water body provides an excellent playground for the yachtsman.

Power Projects – The Creation

Approximately 76 miles upstream from Montreal and at the east end of Cornwall Island we reach the International Boundary, and enter what has become known as the International Rapids section. This section extends for 47 miles to a point four miles east of Prescott, Ontario, and involves a difference in elevation of 92 feet. This section was undoubtedly the key one in the whole of the St Lawrence Seaway development from the stage of the initial suggestion of a deep seaway to the creation of what we see today as we travel through the locks and canals and open waterways. It was the key section because it is an international waterway. Through it runs the boundary between Canada and the United States. For this reason negotiation and agreement were necessary before the great power potential of the St Lawrence could be developed. The tremendous head pond or reservoir of water behind the St Lawrence Power Dam, the Long Sault Dam and the Eisenhower Lock provides an excellent navigable stretch of water which meant great savings in dredging and excavation.

It is here that the Hydro-Electric Power Commission of Ontario and the Power Authority of the State of New York have developed 2,200,000 horse-power of electricity by using 81 feet of a 92-foot drop in the water level between Lake Ontario and the St Lawrence Power Dam at Cornwall. They did this by building a major power dam across the main channel of the St Lawrence between Barnhart Island and the Canadian mainland, a control dam below the Long Sault Rapids, another control dam close to Iroquois, and the flooding of an area 38,000 acres in extent. This flooding has created a lake some 30 miles in length, and from 1½ to 4 miles in width.

The St Lawrence Seaway Development Corporation was responsible for the construction of navigation facilities on United States territory, which enabled shipping to by-pass the power dams and be lifted a total of 81 feet. The St Lawrence Seaway Authority was responsible for the construction of the Iroquois Lock and Canal on Canadian territory. The Iroquois Lock lifts shipping from the level of the power pool almost to the level of Lake Ontario, a difference of between 1 and 6 feet.

Let us continue our journey through the International Rapids

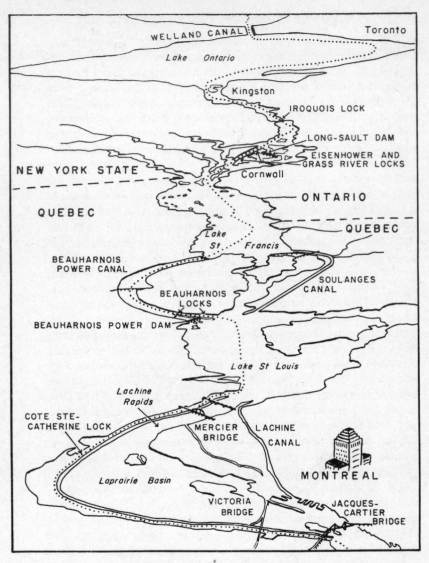

3 GREAT LAKES — ST LAWRENCE
The dotted line shows the route of the Seaway

section. It takes the average vessel about 6 hours to traverse the locks, canals, artificial lake and river channel. At the point where our vessel swings south of Cornwall Island, a second deep channel branches off to the north. It was necessary for two purposes. It is a compensation for the navigation dredging in the south channel and it provides deep navigation to the port of Cornwall. Having been located on the old St Lawrence canal system, Cornwall was entitled to these navigation facilities, but in addition Canada anticipates 27-feet navigation entirely on the Canadian side of the boundary in the future.

The south channel which we now follow between Cornwall Island and the United States mainland is crossed by a high-level suspension bridge which provides highway access between Cornwall and Massena, New York, and a clearance of 120 feet for shipping. Canada's St Lawrence Seaway Authority built the substructure of this bridge and its United States equivalent built the superstructure. The sharing of costs on the construction of this bridge, which was in proportion to the actual lengths of the bridge in each country, provides a very good example of how costs were shared on construction in many parts of the International Rapids section. The main suspension of the bridge is 3,840 feet long and it is carried on two 232-foot-high towers each standing on two piers in the river course. This bridge replaced the Roosevelt International Bridge, which was a low-level combined road and rail bridge carrying the New York Central Railway. Initial plans called for the relocation of this railway, but the New York Central decided to abandon its railway service between Cornwall and the United States, so that a high-level road bridge was possible. It was opened in December 1958.

Immediately on our left, that is, on the United States mainland, two large industrial plants are noticeable. These are the new General Motors plant and a new Reynolds Metals plant, both using power from the new St Lawrence Power Dam.

Two miles upstream from the suspension bridge we enter the Bertrand H. Snell Lock, the first of two locks in the United States territory which raise our ship from the level of Lake St Francis to the level of the power pool. The normal lift at the Snell Lock is about 40 feet. Ahead of us is 10 miles of canal, known as the Wiley-Dondero Ship Channel, and another 40–45 feet lift via the Dwight

The St Lawrence Seaway

D. Eisenhower Lock. Approximately a third of the way along the canal we pass under massive overhead transmission cables which carry power·to many parts of upper New York State, including Plattsburgh on the west shore of Lake Champlain and the giant plant of the Aluminum Company of America at Massena, which can be seen a few miles to the south of the canal. This plant originally obtained its power from the Cedar Rapids power-house in the Soulanges section. On our right, covering what remains of the mainland and Barnhart Island, is the St Lawrence State Park, a very pleasantly landscaped recreational area. It is reached from the south via a tunnel under the Eisenhower Lock.

At this point we sail out into the huge lake which was created by the damming of the St Lawrence. It extends some 30 miles upstream in international waters to the Iroquois Lock. This vast lake is studded with islands, both large and small. At one or two points in this 30-mile section the channel had to be excavated across these islands before inundation took place, but over the greater part of the lake the depth is far in excess of what is needed for safe navigation. On the Canadian side many of these small islands which were originally small hills and ridges on the mainland have been joined together as well as to the mainland by a series of causeways, to form the Canadian counterpart of the St Lawrence State Park. Dozens of yachts, speedboats, and launches are to be seen on the surface of the lake, bearing testimony to the very important recreational role of this great development. We catch glimpses here and there of the new towns and the relocated towns on the Canadian mainland. Rehabilitation was carried out on a much larger scale on the Canadian side because settlement was much more dense than along the northern limits of New York State. This very important phase of the Seaway development will be described in detail in the next chapter.

The Iroquois Lock and canal is reached approximately twelve hours after leaving Montreal. This lock is needed to enable shipping to by-pass the Iroquois Control Dam, which controls the flow of water from Lake Ontario 80 miles upstream. The maximum lift on this lock will be 6 feet. The Iroquois Lock was the first of the seven Seaway locks to be completed. On 22nd November 1957 the Hon. George Hees, Canadian Minister of Transport, moved the lever on the control panel to open the lower sector gates for the first ship, the

C.G.S. *Grenville*, a Federal Government lighthouse tender, to enter the lock chamber.

In the St Lawrence upstream from the lock there is on the average only one foot difference in elevation between Iroquois and the eastern limit of Lake Ontario; in fact, the water body here is rather a lengthy arm of Lake Ontario. In the section by-passed originally by the old Galop Canal considerable channel excavation was necessary because a series of rocky islands occupy the greater part of the major channel. Farther to the west scattered rock shoals had to be removed. This work was carried out by both United States and Canadian Seaway Authorities.

THOUSAND ISLANDS – LAKE ONTARIO

Deep water is available along a marked course in the Thousand Islands section and across Lake Ontario, so that no construction and only a little dredging was carried out, except on the approaches to several of the ports on the Canadian side of the boundary, such as Brockville and Kingston, where extensive dredging was necessary.

The journey from Prescott through the Thousand Islands and across Lake Ontario to the entrance of the Welland Canal takes approximately fifteen hours. Most of this section will be completed during the first night of our journey.

WELLAND CANAL

As the Seaway locks and canals passed through so far were patterned on the proportions of the Welland Canal, it is obvious that little improvement was necessary in this section. Dredging of the pre-Seaway 25-foot channel to the regulation 27 feet was all that was called for. The eight locks required no alteration. The average upbound passage from Lake Ontario to Lake Erie takes about eleven hours. Our journey would be faster if it were not for several long waits. Only three of the Welland's eight locks are twin locks, so that at five of the locks there is always a chance of meeting a downbound vessel, and if it arrives first it enters the lock first, which means a wait of at least 45 minutes. The journey in the opposite direction takes three hours less, i.e. about $8\frac{1}{2}$ hours, because it is the downstream direction and locks empty a lot faster.

The St. Lawrence Seaway

Sailing out into Lake Erie, we are approximately halfway between the entrance of the St Lawrence River and the lakehead ports on Lake Superior. Most of the spectacular seaway construction is behind us. Ahead of us work on the Seaway is still going on. Chiefly because Congress did not authorise work in this section until March 1956, channel deepening and lock improvement is not yet complete, so that 27-feet navigation for upbound vessels will probably not be available for a year or two yet. Although this work is not spectacular, it is extremely important. The downbound channels between Lake Superior and Lake Huron, between Lake Huron and Lake Michigan, and between Lake Huron and Lake Erie, must be deepened from 25 feet to 27 feet and channels must be widened. Additional anchorage area is also called for on the lower and upper ends of the St Mary's River. The only construction involved is the replacement of the existing Poe Lock on the St Mary's River by a modern lock. The Canadian lock at Sault Ste Marie will also be improved at a later date.

The complete journey will take us between three and four days. The Montreal to Lake Erie section is by far the slowest because of the many locks and confined channels. Once our ship is out on the Great Lakes it can travel at maximum speed, which will probably be about 16 knots. Sailing on the Great Lakes, especially on Lakes Superior, Huron and Michigan, is very similar to sailing on the ocean, and a typical severe Great Lakes storm will readily remind one of the Atlantic in heavy seas.

CONSTRUCTION

The story of construction – of bridges, canals, dykes, locks, dams, power-houses and all the other features which make up the Seaway and Power projects – is as interesting and colourful as any similar undertaking anywhere in the world. The following pages deal in some detail with the more spectacular as well as with the less striking though equally essential features of the Seaway and Power projects.

Many of the details of design and construction had been worked out for the preparation of earlier proposals for a seaway so that in many cases these plans simply needed modification. Nevertheless a great deal still needed to be done. That the Seaway and Power projects got under way so rapidly is amazing when one considers the number of authorities which had to be consulted before any plans could be confirmed.

The description that follows is selective. There has been no attempt to describe every phase of construction. A start will be made at the downstream end of the Seaway project.

ORGANISATION

It was on 13th May 1954 that the United States Congress passed the Wiley-Dondero Act. Approximately a month later the final decisions were reached which permitted the power and navigation development of the International Rapids section to proceed. The St Lawrence Seaway Act was proclaimed in July. In August Canada and the United States agreed that the Seaway would be ready for 27-foot draft traffic in the spring of 1959. This left just over four years in which to plan and execute the entire operation. It is a remarkable achievement that the job was finished on time, considering the relatively short period available, the severity of the winter months, and the complexity of the overall operation. Highest praise must go to those men responsible for scheduling all the construction work. When it was realised that there were a hundred or more contracts involved in the construction of the navigation facilities alone, it will be appreciated that they had to be scheduled very skilfully. All contractors had to work to a very tight schedule. Seaway authorities had to keep a constant check on the progress of all work, because frequently adjacent contracts were dependent on each other. The contractors constructing locks had to build concrete mixer plants on the spot to enable them to pour concrete at a specified minimum hourly output. Excavation contractors had to provide equipment capable of a specified total rate of excavation. Seaway authorities could take no chances. Jobs had to be finished on time and they generally were. Many were finished months ahead of schedule, often as a result of working continuously through the winter months. The contract for the overland channel from the upstream end of the Côte Ste Catherine Lock, for example, was completed eight months ahead of schedule.

In dividing up the many miles of channel into reasonable-sized contracts and in the scheduling of commencement and completion dates, many factors had to be taken into consideration. Certain excavation contracts were commenced before others because the type of rock excavated was needed either as concrete aggregate for construction jobs or as the rock shoulder on dykes. Contracts in the Caughnawaga Indian Reserve were awarded later than many others because there was considerable delay in the obtaining of rights to enter the Reserve. Typical of many of the contracts awarded was Contract No. 1. Awarded on 25th October 1954, this contract covers the section between the Jacques Cartier and Victoria Bridges. It was valued at $2,314,500, and it required the excavation of some 7,600 feet of the Seaway channel and construction of the dyke. It was to be completed by 30th June 1957. One of the largest contracts in the Lachine section was granted on 26th August 1955. It called for the construction of Côte Ste Catherine Lock, approach canals, and the excavation of a turning basin downstream from the lock. It had to be completed by 31st July 1958.

The success obtained resulted from excellent co-ordination of the work of the many contractors and the co-ordination of construction with the maintenance of all existing services including railways, highway traffic, power and communication lines, water supply and sewers.

THE COST

The total cost of the entire Seaway and Power project is not yet known, but it will probably be in the vicinity of $1,200,000,000. The cost of the Power project was approximately $650,000,000 shared about equally by the New York State Power Authority and the Hydro-Electric Power Commission of Ontario. The United States expenditure on navigation facilities, including the improvement of navigation channels in the Upper Great Lakes, added up to about $300,000,000, while Canada spent somewhat more, about $350,000,000, on navigation facilities. Combining the Seaway and Power projects undoubtedly saved many millions.

CONSTRUCTION OF DYKES AND EXCAVATIONS

In all 50 miles of dykes had to be built and 51,000,000 cubic yards of rock, clay, silt and sand had to be excavated. These two tasks in the construction of canals would appear to be relatively straightforward and in parts of the Seaway they were, but there were many problems involved, some expected, some entirely unforeseen. To the layman it was all exciting, and on weekends and during the long summer evenings along the St Lawrence valley thousands sat or stood for hours watching the drills, the blasting, the giant shovels and Euclid trucks at work. Equally as fascinating was the procedure followed when channels had to be excavated along the existing river bed. And the problems were not all to do with rock and river, but with people, too. People once lived where Seaway channels now exist. For centuries people have piped their water supplies from the great river and have fished it summer and winter. The excavation and movement of millions of tons of rock and sand and silt meant dust, especially in summer, and people consider dust a nuisance.

The Seaway engineer faced with the construction of canals found a multitude of problems upon his hands. With some he had had previous experience on other construction jobs, but many were entirely new. Many of his problems resulted from the fact that 80 per cent of the excavated length of the Seaway channel was in the bed of the St Lawrence River. For this reason detailed information on soil and rock conditions along the channel was almost completely lacking before 1952, when final design studies were commenced. Intensive work between 1952 and 1958 on the design and construction of the Seaway and Power projects involved the application of soil and foundation engineering practice on a scale unsurpassed on a single project – in Canada, at least. The connection of soil and foundation difficulties with the construction of canals is a traditional one. The function of canals inevitably locates them on low ground and interferes with natural geologic processes. Difficulties in the construction of some of the world's great canals – the Kiel Canal and the Panama Canal, for example – have resulted in special investigations which have advanced the engineers' knowledge of soil mechanics.

One of the problems the Seaway engineer ran into resulted from the lowering of ground water in areas adjacent to the Seaway when he excavated into the shale which underlies most of the glacial till in the region. Along the south shore from just above Victoria Bridge to beyond Caughnawaga there were several hundred residences and other buildings drawing water from wells. When the ground water table was lowered the wells ran dry. In these areas the Seaway channel is located a considerable distance out from shore, so it was not expected that excavation would interfere with the ground water on the south shore. During this period of construction water supply to these settlements was delivered to individual residents by tank trucks with 250-gallon tanks furnished by the Seaway Authority. Around the shoreline of the village of Caughnawaga the Seaway channel was excavated entirely in rock. It was expected that wells in this section would run dry, and consequently the construction contractors provided for the supply of water to the local residents, but the wells did not run dry. An intensive drilling programme over a distance of 120 miles along the river made possible the mapping of most water-bearing layers of rock, which might have proven difficult for construction.

In general, soils, glacial overburden and bedrock were favourable to most construction operations. The vast deposits of glacial till, ranging in thickness up to 100 feet, which are to be found in many parts of the St Lawrence Lowland, proved to be a most useful construction material. The till was used in nearly all dykes and as a fill in all rock cofferdams. In some areas, and especially at the site of the Iroquois Canal, the till proved to be as dense as concrete. Drilling and excavation costs soared far above estimates. Some of the heavy marine clays also provided problems in construction operations, but when the clays became weathered they were used satisfactorily as fill in the dykes.

In the Laprairie Basin and St Lambert sections shale is predominant as bedrock. The shale is a cemented, non-plastic rock which disintegrates into angular particles on exposure to air. It was thought at first that weathering would reduce the shale to an impervious condition and that it would be useless as fill in the pervious zones of the dykes, but investigation of old shale dumps in the district indicated that it remained pervious though disintegrated.

The rapid disintegration of shale also proved a problem elsewhere. All the piers of the Victoria Bridge and most of the piers of the Jacques Cartier Bridge stand directly upon shale. It was thus necessary in the excavation of the channel between piers of both bridges to proceed with great caution. Only 12-foot sections of the shale underlying the piers were exposed at a time. Concreting would be completed and then another 12-foot face could be exposed. This procedure in both cases took a whole year, but it was not until this work was complete that any of the steel superstructure could be modified. The other lock structures were founded on dolomitic limestone at

Iroquois and sandstone at Beauharnois, and apart from the very great hardness of these rocks, and consequently the high costs of drilling, they provided no problems as foundation.

The materials discussed above – the glacial till, the shale and limestone – were all ideal for the building of dykes. Dykes were designed to utilise the excavated materials to the maximum. A typical dyke section consists of an impervious core of compacted glacial till, between pervious shoulders of broken shale or limestone. This combination has so far proved to be ideal. The dykes must confine the navigation channel and keep its water level constant in face of fluctuating river levels. They must also withstand the tremendous pressure of ice ridges in winter.

COFFERDAMS

A new word, 'cofferdam', has been added to the vocabulary of tens of thousands of visitors to Seaway sites. As these thousands watched during the autumn of 1954, and particularly during the summer of 1955, giant Euclid trucks and earthmovers proceeded to dump rock and till into the channel of the St Lawrence. They built themselves a road as they dumped farther and farther out into the river. At a given point, often a mile or more from the south bank of the river, they turned at right angles and gradually enclosed a small section of the St Lawrence. Giant pumps were then set to work, and while the cofferdams held back the waters of the St Lawrence the enclosed bed of the river was pumped dry. The same trucks and bulldozers built roads into the cofferdammed area where drilling, blasting and excavation was commenced.

The two photos facing page 16 show clearly how excavation of the Seaway channel proceeded from this initial operation. This method of excavation was followed for the entire length of the channel across the Laprairie Basin. The outer cofferdam was eventually used as the foundation for the main Seaway dykes. In two areas, upstream from Caughnawaga and at the entrance to the Seaway in Montreal Harbour, because of either the great speed of the river or the greater depth of the rock and till, cofferdams had to be reinforced with steel sheet piling. The silence of many a summer and autumn evening along the south shore of the St Lawrence was broken by the 'thump-thump' of the pile-drivers at work.

The St Lawrence Seaway

All did not go according to plan. When it comes to climate or to the flow of a river we generally think in terms of the average conditions. We rarely take the possible extremes into account. The St Lawrence River at Montreal has always been subject to ice jams and consequent flooding. The construction schedule for work on the Seaway was related to the probable winter conditions, and climatic records for the past fifty years were available. It so happened that the winter conditions of 1955–6 were substantially more severe than any on record – as they were too in 1958–9.

The cofferdams were constructed to withstand probable extreme conditions on the St Lawrence, but in several sections the cofferdams were not high enough. In the winter of 1955–6 the St Lawrence rose to record heights. In these sections, as in others, it was planned to flood the already excavated channel during the winter months in order to avoid large volumes of erosion which might occur if the St Lawrence and its ice happened to overflow the cofferdam. Unfortunately, when the latter did occur in one section where the cofferdam had not been flooded on time a large quantity of material was washed into the channel and subsequently had to be re-excavated. In the section between the Victoria Bridge and Laprairie the contractor responsible decided to work throughout the winter. He built a higher cofferdam than was ordinarily required, and even then, in the winter of 1956–7, the water level rose to within a foot or two of the crest of the cofferdam; there was no overflow and excavation proceeded according to plan all winter.

HYDRAULIC MODELS

During the course of design and construction of Seaway and Power facilities hydraulic models were used to test features which had been evolved from calculations and analysis. At Ville Lasalle near Montreal the Seaway Authority constructed an Hydraulic Laboratory Building in which models of the Lachine Rapids section and the Montreal Harbour section were constructed. At the National Research Council Hydraulic Laboratory at Ottawa a model was constructed of the section of the St Lawrence from the Barnhart Island power-houses to Lake St Francis, and another model reproduced the typical Seaway lock. In all cases each model was so constructed that it behaved in a manner similar to the structure it represented.

Power Projects – The Creation

The two Seaway models at Ville Lasalle represented at a scale of $\frac{1}{200}$ of the actual river, the critical sections of the river between Lake St Louis and Montreal Harbour. All Seaway features were represented as they were constructed, and by measurements of flow, by means of specially designed gauges and meters and a careful analysis of the results, the pre-construction calculations of eventual force and direction of flow and depth of the St Lawrence at critical points could be checked. The model of the Montreal Harbour section was used in designing and locating the dykes at the entrance to the Seaway in order to check that vessels entering the Seaway would do so without encountering dangerous currents. Both models were used to show how any future power development at Lachine might be integrated with Seaway construction.

At Ottawa the model lock reproduced in detail every phase of the operation of a Seaway lock, and was used in the development of a hydraulic system that now enables a ship to pass through the lock in a minimum of time and with a maximum of security.

The models of the International Rapids section showed such things as what level would be flooded behind the power dam; how much water would flow over a spillway of the dam when a certain number of gates are open; how channels in the Cornwall area could best provide a broad, slow-flowing waterway leading to the Snell Lock and at the same time provide assurance that navigation facilities on the Canadian side of the river at Cornwall could be constructed when required with a minimum of difficulty.

Throughout the period of construction every change in the channel and in the direction and speed of flow of the river was immediately recorded and appropriate adjustments made in the models. This work was of tremendous value to the Seaway engineers.

THE LACHINE SECTION

In 1948 a Board of Engineers recommended to the Canadian Government two schemes for the development of hydroelectric power and navigation, and one scheme for navigation alone, within the Lachine section. The St Lawrence Seaway Authority adopted the latter, the same in all respects as the one contained in the report of 1948, except that it was decided to construct the canal on the south side of the Laprairie Basin rather than on the north. There were four outstanding reasons for placing the canal on the south side of the Laprairie Basin: (i) it would permit the extension of the Montreal Harbour to the south shore and stimulate the development of an important industrial area adjacent to Montreal; (ii) it was considered that it would be easier to cope with the highway and railway traffic communication between Montreal and the south shore at the south end of the Jacques Cartier and Victoria Bridges, both during the period of construction and in the future; (iii) it would avoid the navigation of the St Mary's current and the congested area of the Montreal Harbour.

The tasks and problems of the Seaway engineers were many and varied. One of the most spectacular projects in the whole of the Seaway development was the modification of the existing bridges. This work was necessary to provide a clearance of 120 feet through the Seaway. Within the Lachine section seven bridges had to be modified. Lift spans had to be constructed into five rail or road-and-rail bridges. The Jacques Cartier and Honore Mercier Bridges, which are highway bridges only, had to be modified to provide the 120-foot clearance. Not only were these projects spectacular, but they were carried out with very little interruption of existing traffic. In fact, there was not a day when road or rail traffic was stopped completely.

The Jacques Cartier Bridge, constructed in 1928, is the major line of communication for road traffic across the St Lawrence at Montreal. There are two sections to the bridge. At the north end, between the north shore and St Helen's Island, there is a 1097-foot-long cantilever section, providing a clearance of 120 feet for shipping entering Montreal Harbour. Between St Helen's Island and the south shore there is a ramp-type bridge. The permanent raising of this southern end and the replacement of a span to provide the necessary clearance was probably one of the largest operations of its kind ever undertaken. The pre-Seaway bridge had a clearance of approximately 40 feet between the lower chord of the existing deck truss span and high-water level. It was thus necessary to provide an additional 80 feet of clearance between piers No. 9 and No. 10, where the Seaway intersects the bridge structure. The first 30 feet were obtained by replacing the existing deck truss span by a truss span above road level (see Plate 3). The remaining 50 feet required were obtained by jacking the bridge structure whilst increasing the elevation of the supporting piers. The jacking was carried out in progressive stages

14 The graceful arc of the Long Sault Dam, across the southern channel of the St Lawrence. The Long Sault Dam helps to maintain the level of the power pool behind the power dam downstream. The St Lawrence power dam and the city of Cornwall can be seen in the left background.

The United States locks in the International Rapids Section.

15 *Above:* The first passenger cruise ships in the Dwight D. Eisenhower Lock, September 6th, 1958.

16 *Below:* Construction on the Bertrand H. Snell Lock at the downstream end of the Wiley-Dondero Ship Channel. These two locks lift ships to a total of 81 feet from the level of Lake St Francis to the power pool.

without interruption to the flow of traffic over the bridge. The requirement of a maximum grade of approximately 4 per cent on the roadway from each end of the new span meant that adjoining spans had to be raised varying amounts, as did the piers. The jacking was accomplished by eighteen 500-ton hydraulic jacks and twelve 400-ton jacks. Heavy steel weldments called 'climbing jacks' were placed alongside of, and to act in place of, each pier section. The main jacking operation was carried out in the following way. First of all, there were three surface sections on the climbing jacks. As pressure was applied to the climbing jacks the span end would be raised 6 inches at a time, and precast concrete blocks were placed under the two outer sections of each climbing jack. A third concrete block would then be placed under the base of the hydraulic jack at the centre. The span would then have been raised 6 inches and the operation could be repeated. All four jacking points on one pier were raised simultaneously, but the operation would not be repeated until the adjacent span and temporary pier had been raised 6 inches. When the span-ends over any pier had been raised 2 feet the permanent concrete pier would be built up to bridge level. This operation was carried out so gradually and so skilfully that many passing motorists had no idea that the work was under way.

The replacement of the old deck truss span by a new through truss span between piers No. 9 and No. 10 was one of the most exciting moments of the whole Seaway project. Falsework was built on the downstream and upstream sides of the bridge. The new span was constructed on the upstream falsework. The supports of both spans were then set on giant rollers, which moved upon a system of rails. By means of hydraulic jacks the 1,500 tons of the old span and the 1,600 tons of the new span, each span being 250 feet in length, were moved in a horizontal direction downstream, a distance of 78 feet. The new span was then secured in place and the old one dismantled. Only four and a half hours were needed for the whole operation, which took place on 20th October 1957, and that was the only occasion when traffic flow was halted for more than a few minutes.

To maintain the required grade level at the south end of the bridge, the abutment had to be extended a considerable distance. While the two southernmost spans were being raised and the abutment extended temporary Bailey bridges and access roadways were installed to divert traffic. The rock fill needed for the abutment and the extensive traffic circle at the south end was obtained from the material excavated from the channel. The efficient traffic circle now in operation is an excellent example of the facilities produced by the co-operation of the Seaway with the National Harbours Board, the provincial government, and the local municipality.

VICTORIA BRIDGE

No less spectacular was the modification of the Victoria Bridge. Alterations were complicated by the fact that this bridge is a combined road-and-rail bridge. There are roadways on each side of a double-track railroad. Actually, the Seaway development hastened the conversion of the downstream section of the bridge from a tramway to a roadway, providing one-way roadways on each side of the centre railtrack.

The Victoria Bridge was originally built as a tubular, single-track railway bridge across the St Lawrence. The piers of the bridge were modified from time to time to enable it to withstand the tremendous pressure of ice which builds up during winter in the Laprairie Basin immediately upstream. The bridge took its pre-Seaway form in 1898. It is today the property of the Canadian National Railway. The objective of the Seaway engineers at the Victoria Bridge was twofold: one, to provide a lift span in the bridge to allow ships to pass through the St Lambert Lock, and, two, to devise a scheme whereby there would be as little interruption of road and rail traffic as possible.

It was obvious at the beginning that a lift span was necessary, rather than an overhead bridge, because, unlike the Jacques Cartier Bridge, the Victoria Bridge is a low-level bridge. A high-level bridge would have required several miles of approach span to keep within relatively flat maximum permissible railroad grade. The erection of the lift span presented unusual problems because heavy railway traffic continued to operate over the span while work was in progress. To do the job it was necessary first of all to construct a 150-ton capacity guy derrick, which was mounted on a 182-foot steel tower standing on the floor of the lock. The top of the derrick was 384 feet above the lock floor. Falsework designed to support both trains and the existing structure were erected under the existing bridge. The weight of the existing span was then gradually transferred to the falsework. The existing structure of the span was then dismantled, with the existing railway bridge floor being removed in sections under one track at a time, to permit railway traffic on the other track. Pre-assembled deck and track units were lifted into place by means of the derrick. The construction of the upper portions of the lift span was then carried out, with Bailey bridges and a thick timber mat providing protection for passing trains. Uninterrupted road traffic also had to be provided for while the lift span was being erected. This immediate problem was solved by Canadian National Railway and Seaway engineers in the course of finding a solution to the major problem of maintaining continuous road and rail traffic while the Seaway is in operation. A plan was devised whereby a second lift bridge, located just beyond the upper lock-gates, was constructed to carry road and rail traffic while the lower lift span was up to allow shipping to pass. By using the canal banks and additional embankments road traffic will be diverted from the main bridge to the upper lift span, whilst a diversionary bridge will be constructed for rail and traffic. The latter will be diverted from the main bridge about two-thirds of the way across from the island of Montreal. Uninterrupted road traffic will be allowed for by means of an overpass at the railway diversion.

Let us follow the full procedure whilst a ship is using the St Lambert Lock. Remember that there is two-way road and rail traffic and that the double rail tracks divide the two roadways, one for southbound and one for northbound traffic. Immediately prior to the arrival of a ship at the downstream end of the St Lambert Lock, road and rail traffic would be passing in two directions from the south end and the north end of this main bridge. As the ship reaches the lock and the barrier is raised, traffic lights will divert road traffic at three points and rail traffic at two points. Actually rail traffic will have been redirected well ahead of road-traffic diversions because of the greater distances involved in a rail traffic diversion. Southbound rail traffic at a given signal will follow the upstream diversionary bridge which links up with the upstream lift bridge and a diversionary overpass. This route will also be followed by northbound rail traffic diverted from a point close to St Lambert station. Southbound road traffic will be diverted from the north end of the downstream lift span along an embankment to the upstream lift bridge, and will from this point move directly to the south shore. Northbound road traffic arriving at the south end of the bridge will be directed by lights to the upstream lift bridge. After crossing the lift bridge traffic will follow the north dyke wall and pass under the main bridge to loop back up to bridge level again on the downstream side, beyond the uplifted lift span. It will then continue across the bridge to the Island of Montreal. When the ship has been raised 15 feet and is ready to pass through the upstream lock-gates, traffic will be rediverted to the main bridge and the lift bridge will be raised.

Thus uninterrupted traffic, both road and rail, will have been provided for by the simple arrangement of two lift spans, embankments and a diversionary rail bridge. At least this is what the engineers have planned. The system as yet has not been fully tested. In the opinion of one who has travelled for several years back and forth across the Victoria Bridge by car, bus and train, it will be quite remarkable if the system operates perfectly.

THE POWER PROJECT

At about 4 a.m. on 1st July 1958 an engineer at the Iroquois Control Dam pushed a button which set in operation gantry cranes, which in turn lifted large steel gates to allow the waters of the St Lawrence through in full force. They had been kept under control for three years while construction was going on downstream. At 8 a.m. on the same day, less than 10 miles downstream, these waters rose to a level behind the giant cofferdam which blocked off a 2-mile construction area, at which point over 30 tons of explosives were detonated to blast two great gaps in the cofferdam. The waters of the St Lawrence rushed through the gaps to coalesce again and form a great wave which carried everything before it as it moved downstream, towards the power dam. Three days later the waters of the St Lawrence rose to the level required for testing generating equipment. Within a week of the initial breakthrough of the St Lawrence at the Iroquois Control Dam the first electric power was supplied to consumers in New York State and Ontario. It was 1913 when Ontario Hydro first began to investigate the power possibilities of the St Lawrence in the International Rapids Section. Forty-five years later this power was harnessed. By 1960 New York State and Ontario will share equally a total output of about 2.2 million horse-power.

Power Projects – The Creation

As the waters of the St Lawrence rushed through the gaps in the cofferdam they also began inundation of approximately 38,000 acres of Canadian and United States territory. Slightly more was lost on the Canadian side. Town-sites, valuable farmland, roads and rail tracks and a considerable section of the old St Lawrence canal system disappeared. Some areas are today covered by up to 90 feet of water. Quite obviously all shipping had to be kept out of the area while the power-pool was filling up. The Cornwall-Iroquois section of the St Lawrence was closed to navigation for four days. From 4th July ships began to use the new Seaway facilities in the International Rapids section.

The flow of the St Lawrence River in the International Rapids section has now been fully harnessed. It was not necessary to compromise the ultimate installed capacity of the hydroelectric facilities to provide convenient navigation facilities. The six main structures required for the generation of power and for maintaining water level were all located at points which allowed for the maximum utilisation of the power of the St Lawrence.

The six main structures included:

(1) A power-house across the north channel of the St Lawrence, connecting Barnhart Island and the Canadian mainland.
(2) A power-house spillway dam across the south channel of the St Lawrence from Barnhart Island to the United States mainland. It is known as Long Sault Dam.
(3) A control dam across the river in the vicinity of Iroquois Point to regulate the outflow of Lake Ontario in conjunction with dams downstream.
(4) Dykes as necessary on both sides of the river to retain the pool level at and above Barnhart Island.
(5) A canal closure structure in the Canadian dyke adjacent to the power-house to provide for continuance of 14-foot navigation during the construction period.
(6) A controlled intake at the mouth of the Massena Canal.

In addition, channel enlargement at various locations within the power-pool was necessary, as well as land acquisition for the relocation of highways, railroads and towns.

The St Lawrence Seaway

The St Lawrence Power Dam consists of two power-houses of approximately the same dimensions and design and with identical installed capacity. Together they form a continuous structure which spans the north channel of the St Lawrence between the downstream end of Barnhart Island and a point on the Canadian shore which is approximately a mile from the city of Cornwall. The Canadian power-house is called the Robert H. Saunders–St Lawrence Generating Station, a tribute to a former Ontario Hydro-Electric Commission chairman who was one of the development's most ardent advocates. The American equivalent is known as the Barnhart Island Powerplant. The entire structure consists of a massive concrete intake and the two power-houses, immediately downstream and integral with the intake structure. Thus an integrated concrete dam has been formed which extends in a straight line across the channel for a distance of 3,200 feet. The height of the dam, that is from the deck of the intake structure to its base, is 162 feet. The maximum power head is about 87 feet. Water will enter the dam through grated openings to drive thirty-two turbine-generator units, sixteen on each side of the International Boundary. The power-houses are of the semi-outdoor type. Removable water-tight covers are provided for each of the thirty-two turbines. The turbines are 75,000 horsepower, fixed-blade, propeller type and are connected to 60,000 kVA generators. Power will be generated at the power-houses at approximately 14,000 volts. This voltage will subsequently be stepped up through transformers at the power-house to an efficient voltage for long-distance transmission. From the power-houses the power is carried to switch-yards on each side of the International Boundary, through cables in galleries within the power-house structure.

In New York State the bulk of the power will be used at the large industrial sites immediately to the south of the power development, but power will also be transmitted to outlying settlements in upper New York State. Plattsburgh, 70 miles distant on the west shore of Lake Champlain, will receive St Lawrence power. In Ontario settlements throughout the south-eastern portion of the province will benefit from this latest addition to the extensive Ontario Hydro system. Dykes extending outward from each end of the St Lawrence

Power Projects – The Creation

Power Dam are large dykes of compacted earth-fill. These are an essential part of the vast dam across the St Lawrence system. They are as important as the major power dam itself in maintaining the required level of water within the power-pool. The main dyke on the Canadian side is some 3½ miles long, while on the United States side dykes totalling 17 miles are necessary to restrict the power-pool and to prevent it spreading into adjacent low-lying drainage basins. In all about 25 miles of dam formation in one form or another is necessary to maintain the power-pool.

LONG SAULT DAM

The Long Sault Dam is located entirely within United States territory, and upstream from the power dam. It crosses the south channel of the St Lawrence from the upstream end of Barnhart Island to the United States mainland. It serves to control the level of the water in the power-pool, allowing as necessary any excess amounts to by-pass the power dam by means of the south channel. The Long Sault Dam is a concrete gravity curved-axis spillway structure approximately 2,900 feet long and with a maximum height above the foundations of 145 feet. This dam obtained its name from the magnificent rapids which were located immediately upstream on the north channel, but which have since been inundated by the power-pool.

MASSENA INTAKE

This feature is a concrete intake structure on the south shore of the power-pool about 5 miles upstream from the Eisenhower Lock. It serves to supply water to the town of Massena and to the Alcoa aluminium plant. Prior to the Seaway and Power development water was also supplied to a small power-house at Massena. Today a gate across the intake controls the flow of water.

IROQUOIS DAM

This structure, located some 25 miles upstream from the Long Sault Dam, spans the St Lawrence between Iroquois Point, Canada, and Point Rockway in the United States. The dam's main function is to permit regulation of the outflow of water from Lake Ontario. Under natural conditions a natural rock weir near Chimney Point, a short distance downstream from Ogdensburg, New York, controlled the outflow from Lake Ontario at levels between 242 feet and 250 feet above sea level. The new Iroquois Dam is about 7 miles downstream. It is a buttressed gravity concrete structure with gate-controlled sluiceway openings. Its length is 2,540 feet and its height 67 feet. At the United States end the dam is extended by earthfill dykes, but at the Canadian end the dam connects with the Seaway canal and lock. The canal closure structure is located to the north of the Canadian half of the power dam. This structure was necessary because the Canadian section of the power-pool dyke system crossed the old St Lawrence Canal, which was used for navigation right up until the time of the filling up of the power-pool.

CONSTRUCTION

There are many interesting aspects of the design and actual construction of the Seaway and Power project in the International Rapids section. When man begins to interfere with the complete flow of a river as gigantic as the St Lawrence, quite obviously people are going to sit up and take notice, because many of the people in Canada and the United States are directly concerned with water levels, not only in the St Lawrence itself but in its many tributaries and in the five Great Lakes, which act as a giant reservoir for the St Lawrence. It has been shown earlier that there are six authorities responsible for control of water levels and flow in the Great Lakes–St Lawrence system – the Federal Governments, the International Joint Commission, the St Lawrence River Joint Board of Engineers, the International St Lawrence River Board of Control, and the International Lake Ontario Board of Engineers. These authorities were all very much concerned with what amounted to the same problem – that is, how to regulate the natural streamflow of the St Lawrence at the outlet of Lake Ontario.

It was decided that a set of rules might be drawn up to protect all interests above and below the Seaway and Power projects from artificial changes in the regimen of the river which might cause damage or inconvenience both during construction and in the future. The Department of Transport of the Canadian Government prepared such a set of rules, and these were prescribed by the International Joint Commission to govern the project and the levels of Lake Ontario.

Power Projects – The Creation

The basic rules are as follows:

(*a*) Maintain the fluctuations of the levels of Lake Ontario within the levels that would have resulted in the past, assuming a continuous diversion of 3,200 cubic feet per second at Chicago and present outlet conditions.

(*b*) Maintain without impairment the low-water levels of Montreal Harbour.

(*c*) Maintain low flows during the winter period, 15th December to 31st March, in order that the difficulties of winter power operation are not aggravated.

(*d*) Maintain flows during the first half of April no greater than would naturally occur in order to avoid the danger of aggravating the spring rise in levels during the breakup of the ice below Montreal.

(*e*) Avoid any material increase in the amount and duration of the high discharges during May in order not to aggravate high-water levels in Lake St Louis during the time of high flow.

(*f*) Maintain the monthly mean discharges within the limits as existed in nature.

(*g*) Retard the natural excess outflow during the early summer months in order to raise the ordinary levels of Lake Ontario.

(*h*) Secure the maximum dependable flow throughout the year for power operation.

There are at present several artificial influences affecting the outflow from Lake Ontario. Water is diverted from the watershed at Chicago for sanitary, domestic and industrial uses. It hence flows via the Illinois and Mississippi canal system into the Mississippi River. This diversion has varied greatly in the past, but under existing legal limitations the future diversion is estimated to be about 3,200 cubic feet per second, although recently a request was made for a considerable increase in this amount. As a counterbalance to this diversion of water from the Great Lakes some 5,000 cubic feet per second is diverted into Lake Superior from the Hudson Bay drainage system for logging and power purposes. The waters of Long Lake, which naturally drain into the Kenogami River and ultimately into James Bay, have been partly diverted to the south into Lake Superior. The net effect of the restriction on diversions from the lakes and the importation of water from Hudson Bay will be an increase in the average annual outflow from Lake Ontario as compared with the past. These regulation plans will diminish the ratio of maximum to minimum flows from Lake Ontario to 1·7:1. The maximum monthly mean was 314,000 cubic feet per second and minimum monthly mean 144,000. The comparable figures today are 310,000 and 180,000. In addition, the outflow will be so scheduled that the minimum dependable flow during the autumn and winter months, the period of peak power demand, will be kept above 205,000 cubic feet per second.

Another requirement which has been provided for in the power-pool is the velocity of the water. It is desirable to have a solid sheet of ice cover in winter over the forebay, the water body immediately upstream from the power dam, to prevent running ice from clogging up the intake. Solid ice will not form where the velocity of the water is greater than $1\frac{1}{4}$ to $1\frac{1}{2}$ feet per second, but floating ice will pack against the upstream edge of a sheet already formed with velocities up to about $2\frac{1}{4}$ feet per second. Channel improvements were designed to limit velocities to these values in so far as it was possible.

Thus not only was there the problem of designing Seaway and Power structures to allow for regulation levels, flow and diversion on a long-term basis; many of these regulations had to be adhered to during the period of construction. The normal level of Lake Ontario had to be maintained, as did the flow in the St Lawrence below Barnhart Island. This was not by any means the greatest problem faced by the engineers responsible for the construction of the Seaway and Power facilities. Throughout a four-year period of construction the flow of one of the largest rivers in the world had to be harnessed so that it could be diverted back and forth from the north channel to the south channel as the various construction projects were carried out, and all this without hindrance to navigation.

For this purpose cofferdams were again used. Perhaps the largest ever built was the downstream cofferdam at the power dam site. It was a cellular steel and rockfill cofferdam, with steel cells standing 65 feet high, with diameters of 65 feet. The structure spanned a 3,600-foot gap across the north channel. But the most spectacular construction of a cofferdam and diversion of the river was during the second stage of the construction of the Long Sault Dam. A cofferdam was here required immediately upstream from the famous Long

Power Projects – The Creation

Sault Rapids to divert the entire flow of the north channel, which at this point carried 90 per cent of the flow of the St Lawrence. Not only was the construction of cofferdam 'E', as it was designated, difficult because of the flow of the river, a number of additional factors affected its construction. The old 14-foot draught Cornwall Canal started a short distance from the site of the cofferdam, and a lock is located near the entrance to the canal. Only a 4-foot fluctuation in water level was possible without disturbing navigation. At the west end of Long Sault Island a diversion canal took approximately 25,000 cubic feet per second of water for use in the Massena area. Water level, particularly in winter, had to be watched very carefully. Also, because of construction farther downstream and navigation in Montreal Harbour, there could not be any sudden retention or release of flow. By the use of temporary dykes, two channels excavated through parts of Long Sault Island and, later, a part of the Long Sault Dam, all required water levels were maintained.

The major plan for the whole of the International Rapids section was a magnificently designed and executed operation. Field investigations in the region commenced as long ago as 1913. More recent design studies aided by the hydraulic working models enabled Ontario Hydro and the Power Authority of the State of New York to have basic layout and design data available, ready for field activity soon after the final agreement on the project on 7th June 1954. 'Sod turning' ceremonies took place on 10th August 1954, and soon after that the first two major contracts were awarded. From this stage until the waters of the St Lawrence rose up behind the St Lawrence power dam for the first time, all phases of construction, diversion, excavation, relocation and rehabilitation were very carefully co-ordinated.

These stages will now be followed.

Stage I. The first major project was the construction of two cofferdams in order to de-water the north channel immediately upstream from the power-dam site. One was the very large cofferdam at the power-dam site, and the other a 500-foot cofferdam from Barnhart Island to Sheek Island. They were completed in time for de-watering in June of the following year, 1955. The power-house site was then ready for excavation and construction. The second year, 1955, was devoted almost entirely to excavation and preparation for construction. The third year, 1956, concreting commenced. The first concrete was placed on the Canadian side on 17th February, and on the United States side on 17th April. By this time work was well under way on both sides, with the construction of transformer station, transmission lines, road and railway relocations, as well as dykes and channel improvements in the vicinity of the power dam.

Stage II. This stage, which got under way in 1955, saw work commenced on the Long Sault dam site, the Iroquois Control Dam and many of the Seaway navigation facilities. With the exception of the Iroquois lock and canal the bulk of this work was carried out by the United States authorities. The construction of the Long Sault Dam was a particularly difficult undertaking because water flow could not be completely diverted as in the case of the power dam. Long Sault Dam crosses the St Lawrence at a point where part of the flow of the north channel joins the flow of the south channel. Throughout the entire construction period the whole flow of the St Lawrence passed through the gap which the Long Sault Dam now spans. Construction of the dam was completed in four stages. In the first stage cofferdams provided a dry area for the construction of the first half of Long Sault Dam in the south channel. Above the dry portion a temporary cut diverted the waters of the south channel to the north of the dam site into the north channel.

The second stage saw the extension of the Long Sault Dam across the north channel. It was thus necessary to divert the entire flow through the already constructed half of the dam. A giant cut was made through Long Sault Island to accommodate the flow of the north channel; and, as we have seen, a cofferdam was built in the north channel to divert this flow. A further cofferdam had to be constructed below the site of the second half of the dam to protect it from the waters flowing through the existing half of the dam.

In the third stage all the cofferdams were removed and the river was diverted back to the north channel so that the entire flow of the St Lawrence now passed through the thirty-four tunnel ports in the second half of the spillway. Those in the south half were closed. The final stage saw the closing of discharge tunnels as the water level rose in the power-pool.

Meanwhile, upstream, the Iroquois Control Dam was constructed. The task was not as complicated although again the full flow of the St Lawrence had to be coped with. The southern half of the dam was built on dry land at Rockway Point. Channel improvement immediately upstream from the dam was also possible on dry land. The remainder of the dam was completed by use of cofferdams which dried out the construction site and at the same time diverted the flow of the St Lawrence to the completed southern half of the dam where sluice-gates were open.

Concurrent with these major projects, relocation and rehabilitation went on apace, particularly on the Canadian side of the St Lawrence. These subjects will be dealt with in detail later in this chapter.

Stage III. This stage involved the completion of all the major structures and the filling up of the power-pool, a process which has already been described in detail.

MEN, MACHINES AND MONEY

It is obvious that at any major Seaway or Power construction site during the period 1954–9 there was much of interest and great excitement. There was also colour. There were the varied colours of the underlying sedimentary rocks exposed as channels were excavated, the bright yellows and oranges of the big machines and the multi-coloured helmets of the workmen. At any major site there were thousands of workmen and each group was represented by a different-coloured helmet. From the observation towers provided by the Seaway Authority the workmen with their bright helmets looked like a colourful array of ants swarming over the construction site. In the early stages of any construction project yellow seemed to be the dominant colour. The yellow helmet represented the carpenter. At other stages most colours of the rainbow were represented. A green helmet meant a concrete worker, one shade of blue a steel worker, another an electrician, silver a mechanic, and white signified authority or perhaps a visiting administrative officer.

In the summer of 1957, which witnessed the period of peak employment, there were approximately 22,000 persons employed on all phases of the Seaway and Power projects. There were four chief groups involved: (1) the administrative officers of the four Seaway and Power Authorities; (2) the 'authorities'' professional engineers; (3) the contractors and their engineers; and (4) the many skilled and unskilled labourers they employed.

The four 'authorities' alone employed close to 500 professional engineers. Most of these men were Canadians or Americans, but the project attracted a great number of engineers from overseas, many of whom immigrated, particularly to Canada, for that purpose. Others came to the project specially to gain experience which would be of value to them in their home country. Young engineers who were from Australia and New Zealand, for example, just out of engineering school, who gained valuable experience and considerably enhanced their professional standing by working on a number of construction jobs. But the majority of the engineers and labourers were Canadians and Americans, men who had had considerable experience on big construction jobs around the continent and overseas. Many of the men came to the highest wages they had ever been paid. It was not uncommon for an unskilled labourer working a ten-hour day to earn $450 a month. Semi-skilled wages were correspondingly higher. Most men worked a ten-hour shift with little or no time for rest. Even in winter on many tasks they worked day and night, frequently with temperatures far below zero.

Amongst the most colourful and perhaps even amongst the most experienced workmen on the various Seaway projects were the Iroquois Indians from the Caughnawaga Reserve, through which a part of the Seaway channel passes. When the Canadian Pacific Railway Bridge at Caughnawaga was constructed in the 1880s, these Indians gained valuable experience as steel workers. Traditionally they had worked as raftsmen on the great timber drives held every spring on the rivers flowing from the Canadian Shield. The timber drives had become fewer so that the Indians appreciated this new form of employment. These Indians are today recognised as among the outstanding high steel workers in North America. They have worked as highly skilled riveters, riggers and allied tradesmen on many of the lofty structures of the North American continent, such as the Quebec Bridge, the Empire State Building and many a skyscraper in Montreal, Chicago, and Los Angeles.

The labour unions were not slow to attempt to capitalise on the great concentration of manpower at Seaway and Power sites. The International Brotherhood of Teamsters made a bold bid to organise the labourers working for the contractors in the Lachine section, but they were unsuccessful. Actually they campaigned quite successfully until they ran into Miron Freres Ltd., one of the largest and most powerful contractors working on the Seaway. A strike resulted, but after the forceful intervention of the Quebec Premier the Teamsters beat a rapid retreat. From this point the Canadian Labour Congress in Ottawa took over and a council was established, which bargained quite successfully for all labour. The contractors set up a similar organisation which worked in comparative harmony with the Congress council of unions.

And what of the contractors? Again they came chiefly from Canada and the United States. Many large existing contracting firms submitted bids on tenders, but there were also many successful bids from 'joint venture' groups composed of leading construction companies who combined to bring together special skills, experience and special equipment. Most of the American work was carried out by American firms, while Canadian firms were the successful bidders on the north side of the International Boundary. There were some, bankruptcies amongst the contractors and some losses. In the early stages of excavation and construction many contractors bid far too low to show any reasonable profit. This was due in part to their desire for publicity through being associated with a great international project. In part, losses were due to the exceptionally high costs encountered in the excavation of some of the very hard rock and in the handling of heavy marine clay and dense glacial till. Several claims for additional compensation to contractors were made. There were certainly very few fortunes made on the project.

REHABILITATION AND RELOCATION

This phase of the Seaway and Power projects reached much greater proportions in Canada than in the United States, because the Canadian section of the St Lawrence Valley is densely settled, with a considerable number of urban centres, highways and railways, whereas in the United States the area inundated was quite sparsely populated and there were no urban centres.

In all, 20,000 acres of Canadian territory and 18,000 acres of United States territory were lost to the power-pool. This area included land along shorelines as well as whole islands and parts of islands in the St Lawrence River. Affected by this loss of land were 6,500 Canadians in the villages of Iroquois, Aultsville, Farran's Point, Dickinson's Landing, Wales, Moulinette, Mille Roches and one-third of the town of Morrisburg, as well as 360 farms. In the United States 225 farm families and 500 summer cottage owners had to be displaced. In addition, on the Canadian side 18 cemeteries, a number of historical monuments, major transport and communication facilities such as Ontario Provincial Highway No. 2, the double-track main line of the Canadian National Railway, and power and telephone lines had to be relocated.

Many people were sorry to see historical sites disappear, and there was some reluctance to sell properties that in many cases had been in the family for five or six generations, but there were very few if any at all who were not delighted to see Provincial Highway No. 2 disappear under many feet of water. This narrow, winding road had proven irksome and frustrating to many a motorist over the last two or three decades. It is amazing that such a road remained for so long as the main highway connection between Toronto and Montreal.

Ontario Hydro first presented their plans for rehabilitation in the summer of 1954, but it took nearly a year to convince the majority of the inhabitants that they had to go and that they were being offered 'a fair deal' by the authorities. Even today there are the few who resent being moved, some who even left the region in disgust rather than have anything to do with the new communities and the modern facilities that go with them. Once the Ontario Hydro made their 'psychological' breakthrough – that is, once they had convinced the majority that there were many advantages to the relocation and reorganisation of their communities, that the move had to be made anyway, and that they were all thereby participating in an historic event – great enthusiasm was shown by the majority. This enthusiasm was reflected in the large sign placed alongside the main highway outside the town of Iroquois, which stated 'We must go, but watch us grow'.

Ontario Hydro's plan for relocation and rehabilitation called for the creation of three new communities, the addition of a suburb to one existing community, the removal of approximately 525 houses to the new town sites, the complete replacement of larger buildings such as stores, churches, etc., the consolidation of most of the existing cemeteries, the relocation of the main highway and the railroad, and the development of a system of parks and roadside park areas with an Historic Centre located centrally.

The Iroquois Canal and Control Dam.

7 *Above:* Shipping commenced using the Seaway facilities in the International Rapids Section in July 1958, following the creation of the power pool. The 2,540 foot long Control Dam controls the flow of the St Lawrence at the level of Lake Ontario.

8 *Below:* An aerial view of the above scene with the power pool in the background.

19 *Above:* A 'Housemover' in operation. This attractive house in Morrisburg was ⟨the⟩
last one moved from the area to be flooded for the Power Project. In all, *about* ⟨350⟩
houses were moved to new sites.

20 *Below:* An aerial view of the town of Morrisburg, showing some of the new multiple hou⟨sing⟩
units and single homes which were built for those displaced by Power Project flood⟨ing⟩

Power Projects – The Creation

The three new communities in existence today are Iroquois, Ingleside and Long Sault. The new town of Iroquois is located about 1½ miles from the old town site. The town of Ingleside, located 15 miles west of Cornwall, houses the residents of the old villages of Dickinson's Landing, Wales, Farran's Point and Aultsville. Long Sault, which is 8 miles to the west of Cornwall, houses the residents of the old Mille Roches and Moulinette. Only the waterfront business section and a small residential area of Morrisburg were flooded, so that a new subdivision was created to the east of the town to accommodate the displaced structures and to provide new building sites.

In the old communities every resident owner was given the choice of having his house moved to a new site or being compensated for the demolition of the house. If he chose the latter course he was also offered extremely favourable terms for the financing of a new home on a lot of his own choosing in the town site. In fact all those who chose to move were given the opportunity of selecting a new lot. For many a family it was the great experience of a lifetime. First, there was the decision whether to keep the old house or not. If the old house was favoured over a new, modern dwelling, then a lot in the new town site had to be chosen. At this stage the new town site was abandoned farmland and the streets of the new town had not yet been laid out. It was a difficult decision to make. Many must have been the questions asked within the family 'council'. How will our old, two-storeyed home look with two modern dwellings on each side? How is it going to look without the maples and the elms? Who are our neighbours going to be? To remove uncertainty, many families agreed to move in alongside each other.

Now came the move, and for many probably the highlight of this great event. For the purpose of moving all but the larger buildings, Ontario Hydro employed the use of two specially constructed 'house-movers', one of 200-ton capacity and the other with a capacity of 100 tons. The larger machine was able to accommodate a 40-foot by 70-foot building. At Iroquois special access roads were built to the new site, because the 'house-movers' required twice the width of a normal road. For the longer and more involved moves into Ingleside and Long Sault, the widening of existing roads or the construction of new roads was not warranted. Special floats were constructed which could use the normal roads. The house was lifted on to the float by one 'house-mover' and lifted off by another at the new foundation. Moves were made with a minimum of inconvenience to the householder. Generally, even crockery was not moved from shelves, and breakfast dishes were occasionally left on the table because of the early arrival of the 'house-mover'. Many a family had breakfast in the old town and lunch in the new. Families were offered several special services to help overcome any inconvenience. 'Stop-over houses' were available to residents while their houses were on the move to the new site. These temporary homes were fully equipped and families using them were only required to take personal items for what usually amounted to an overnight stay. Of course, in advance of any move basements and foundations were constructed and at Ontario Hydro's expense. Modern furnaces were provided at costs far below the prices the householder would ordinarily pay. New porches and garages were also provided. Houses were painted, once at their new location, and complete municipal services, including water, sewers and electricity were installed. Within a short time of the completion of the move roads and pavements were completed and the construction of new buildings such as churches, schools and shopping centres were under way. With the exception of one church, and that the 127-year-old Moulinette Anglican Christ Church, churches, school and business buildings were far too large to be moved. In each new community new shopping centres were provided. Shopping centres were built on the most modern shopping plaza lines, with ample parking space provided. At Iroquois a shopping centre of twenty-four stores and three offices provided accommodation for all merchants from the former community's business section. It is a steel frame construction with an exterior of buff-coloured brick, and store fronts of aluminium and glass.

While construction at major Seaway and Power projects went on apace, the old communities disappeared and new communities arose. By the summer of 1956 the new town of Iroquois took shape. By early summer the last of the dwellings to be moved was on its new foundations and construction of the new facilities was well advanced. The laying out of lawns and the planting of shrubs and trees also took place at the new Iroquois in the spring of 1956. By mid-summer the 'house-movers' were active at Morrisburg and the new town sites of Ingleside and Long Sault. The autumn of 1957 saw most of the houses moved and located, and many new homes under construction. The abandoned town sites were completely cleared by the end of 1957. Throughout the area to be flooded all trees, fences, brush and buildings had to be removed, as they might prove hazardous to navigation in the future. On that very important day in 1958, 1st July, when flooding of 38,000 acres started, the development of new communities was practically complete and hundreds of farm buildings and summer cottages had been relocated. In general, there has been praise for the planning of the whole relocation and rehabilitation programme, but those responsible for the details of the town planning have not been without their critics. Perhaps Ontario Hydro, in a bold and imaginative move, might have insisted on the complete demolition of the old towns and their buildings and the creation of planned communities along modern estate lines. The blending of the old and the new has been a difficult task, and it is doubtful whether the new Iroquois, Ingleside or Long Sault will ever be as aesthetically pleasing as entirely new communities might have been.

PARKS AND RECREATION

Earlier in this chapter reference has been made to the parks and other recreational facilities which have been provided in and around the power-pool area. On the United States mainland immediately north of the Wiley-Dondero Ship channel and on Barnhart Island, the St Lawrence State Park has been created. This entire area has been landscaped and beaches provided in suitable areas.

In Ontario most of the river's shoreline as well as most of the newly created islands became public property once the Seaway and Power development commenced. These appropriated areas are being transformed into parks, scenic drives, recreation facilities, museums and memorials to commemorate a distinguished period in Canadian history. The Ontario–St Lawrence Development Commission, an organisation established and financed by the Ontario Government, is responsible for the entire project. Their planning will follow similar lines to those at Niagara, where pleasant parks and recreational facilities are available. This development also follows the pattern now well established in the United States for the provision of parks and recreational facilities in conjunction with multi-purpose river development and control schemes such as the projects of the Tennessee Valley Authority.

The highlights of the Commission's plans are the creation of Crysler's Battle Memorial Park, located about midway between Ingleside and Morrisburg, the Long Sault Parkway, a wild-fowl sanctuary, a riverside scenic drive, several roadside parks, and facilities for swimming and yachting. Crysler's Battle Memorial Park, more than 2,000 acres in site, will commemorate the Battle at Crysler's Farm, where in 1813 an American force driving towards Montreal was so seriously mauled by Canadian forces that it was forced to return across the St Lawrence. The Obelisk which marked the battle site (now below water) for many generations, has been given a prominent place in the park. In addition to accommodating old structures of historical and architectural interest, in Upper Canada Village, the centre provides a fitting setting for the Pioneer Memorial Cemetery, which contains tombstones from most of the pioneer families of the district. In front of Upper Canada Village an early canal and lock is to be reproduced. A causeway has been constructed from near Long Sault to join up the many islands formed by the flooding. The causeway will reach the north shore again at Ingleside. This scenic drive is known as the Long Sault Parkway.

In Quebec provision has also been made for the landscaping of reclaimed areas. The areas involved are not extensive but they are conveniently located. On the south shore opposite Montreal and between the Victoria and Jacques Cartier Bridges several thousand acres of the old riverbed of the St Lawrence have been reclaimed to be used for recreational purposes.

CHAPTER V

The Future

O n 20th January 1959 the St Lawrence Seaway Authority of Canada announced in a press release that construction of works under its jurisdiction had progressed to a stage which assures that all channels, locks and ancillary structures will be available to shipping at the opening of navigation next spring, although subject in part to a restricted depth of $24\frac{1}{2}$ feet until 1st June, when the specified minimum depth of 27 feet will be available throughout. The slight delay providing the overall depth of 27 feet is due to a shortage of the heavy dredging equipment necessary in sections of the channel and the early advent of winter with unusually severe ice conditions. The Power Authority of the State of New York also has a small amount of dredging to complete in the International Rapids section but otherwise all navigation facilities will be available for use in the spring of 1959.

With the Power project a reality and the Seaway project a near reality, the future of both deserves further consideration. Of the future of the Power project there is no doubt. Its success was assured long before its construction. Both southern Ontario and upper New York State have been short of electric power for a considerable period and the power that was available was relatively expensive. The market therefore existed and it is in part already being satisfied. New industries have been attracted to the region, especially on the United States side of the border. Typical of the industrial plants attracted by cheap St Lawrence power is Reynolds Metals Company's new St Lawrence aluminium reduction plant. This $88 million plant will benefit also from its location on the Seaway. Not only will its raw material be brought directly to the plant from overseas via the Seaway but the latter will also be useful for the distribution of manufactured products within the Great Lakes and St Lawrence region and to overseas markets.

The future of the Seaway is not quite so certain. Many of the claims for the Seaway, especially in the economic field, have already been discussed. These range from unbridled optimism to complete pessimism. In more recent years, especially since construction was commenced, there has been a spate of literature on the economic prospects of the Seaway. This literature includes general treatments, as well as specific studies of bulk commodities, or of the impact of the Seaway upon certain ports and industrial regions. It is the purpose of this final chapter to review the estimates of future commerce upon the Seaway and then to discuss a number of factors which will undoubtedly influence the pattern of commerce and industrial development in the future.

FUTURE COMMERCE

A few general observations can be made first. The role of the St Lawrence Canal system in the economic life of Canada was greatly changed from the role of earlier canals. The 9-foot canals were expected to handle practically all the traffic proceeding west of Montreal. The 14-foot canals were primarily constructed to handle Canadian grain and to capture the grain export trade of the Middle West. In the present century the commerce on the St Lawrence Canal system became more diverse, but it did increasingly tend towards specialisation in the movement of bulk commodities, which included coal, coke, petroleum, timber, etc., apart from the chief commodity, grain. The United States was not concerned to any extent with commerce on the upper St Lawrence, but on the Great Lakes a very considerable movement of iron ore in particular, but also grain, coal, coke, and petroleum, developed. Specialisation and the development of a means of transportation which was both complementary and supplementary to the existing railroad systems were the essence of water transport on the Great Lakes–St Lawrence system prior to 1959.

To what extent is the role of the Great Lakes–St Lawrence waterway likely to change in the future, now that there is 27-foot-deep navigation available to the head of the Great Lakes? Judging from the detailed estimates of future commerce which have been made

ESTIMATES OF FUTURE ST LAWRENCE SEAWAY TRAFFIC

(in thousands of short tons)

Commodity	Average for 1950–4	St Lawrence Seaway Development Corporation		Canadian Department of Trade and Commerce*	Great Lakes St Lawrence Assoc.*	U.S. Dept. of Commerce*	
		1959	1965			min.	max.
Coal and Coke	1,646	3,700	—	4,200	6,000	4,000	4,000
General Cargo	1,362	6,400	—	9,876	5,700	11,038	11,038
Grain	3,481	12,100	—	8,200	10,000	6,500	11,500
Iron Ore	216	10,500	—	20,000	20,000	30,000	37,500
Nonferrous Ore	77	800	—	—	1,000	240	240
Petroleum and Products	1,547	2,300	—	1,091	2,000	6,000	20,000
Wood Pulp and Pulpwood	550	700	—	1,165	1,000	—	—
Total	8,879	36,500	52,000	44,532†	45,700	57,778	84,278

* No precise future date is given in these estimates although they imply an estimate based on a period of 5 to 10 years after the Seaway's completion.
† Revised downward to 31 million tons on 15th April 1965.

both in the United States and Canada, the role of this inland waterway is not likely to change a great deal. All forecasts of future traffic estimate tremendously increased quantities of grain, iron ore, coal and petroleum. Thus it appears that the Seaway is destined to intensify the specialisation which has been the keynote of canal transport during the last century. The major change anticipated is in the amount of general cargo passing through the Seaway. A very considerable increase in the amount of general cargo would result chiefly from the use of the Seaway by a large number of ocean-going freighters.

Most of the estimates of future Seaway traffic deal specifically with the St Lawrence and Welland canals, and do not take into account increased traffic on the upper Great Lakes and particularly between ports of the upper Great Lakes which will probably result from the improvements in port facilities and the increase in depth of harbours, which in turn have been undertaken in anticipation of increased overseas trade. Basically, then, future traffic will increase as a result of the extension and expansion of existing movements.

The specific changes and increases in Seaway traffic which can be expected will now be treated in more detail. The amount of grain shipped to Europe and other areas directly from the grain ports of the upper Great Lakes and the amount carried by lakers down the Seaway to be transhipped at St Lawrence River ports will undoubtedly increase. Estimates of the increase over the average amount of grain which moved down the St Lawrence Canal system between 1950 and 1954 vary from 250 per cent to over 400 per cent. This increase will result from an extension of the tributary area, which will now probably include an extensive area within the United States Middle West in addition to an increased area within the Canadian Prairies, an area which currently exports its grain via the Pacific coast ports. In regard to the diversion of United States grain to the St Lawrence route an American authority, J. R. Hartley, states: 'The tributary area of the Seaway for export to Europe will include all grain-producing land from which land-water freight costs are less than the costs via Gulf or Atlantic ports. . . . Most of the Middle West will be tributary to the Seaway with the Rocky Mountains and the Appalachians as approximate west and east boundaries. The southern dividing line will extend through northern Oklahoma, central

The Future

Missouri and along the Ohio River. . . . The transportation charges via the Seaway route will be from $0·15 to $0·20 per bushel less than the cost over existing eastern routes. However, future competitive rate-cutting may reduce the differential to $0·10 per bushel.' It is obvious that if the tributary area is to increase in extent, then the Atlantic and Gulf ports will suffer. In terms of actual bushels of grain Mr Hartley forecasts a minimum of 161 million bushels and a maximum of 208 million bushels of United States grain which will move through the Seaway by 1960. The maximum amount assumes a diversion of at least a half of the grain which now moves through Atlantic and Gulf ports during the winter months. The magnitude of this diversion does seem to be somewhat exaggerated when one considers the effect of the tolls on the Seaway and the competitive rate-cutting which is most likely to occur where the above magnitude of diversion is possible.

As far as Canadian grain is concerned the future appears a little more certain. In a report of the Montreal Research Council entitled *The Impact of the St Lawrence Seaway on the Montreal Area* it was stated that 'The Seaway route is likely to be carrying about 80 million bushels more of Canadian grain than is currently shipped by vessel from the Lakehead to the Lower St Lawrence ports. This figure is made up of 30 to 35 million bushels from the Pacific ports; 30 million from the Georgian Bay–Lower St Lawrence connection, and about 15 million from the Maritime ports'. The westward extension of the tributary area will result primarily from the reduction in freight charges between the Lakehead and overseas markets, especially Europe, made possible chiefly by the greater distance grain can be moved by the large upper lakers and by the elimination of one or more transhipments. In addition, the greatly increased amount of grain which it will be possible to move on the improved waterway during the summer and autumn months will contribute to this increase in the all-water movement to the east. The latter factor will also be significant in diverting grain from the Georgian Bay and Maritime ports. In the past the bulk of the grain handled by Maritime ports arrived at the Atlantic coast between December and April. It was chiefly grain which could not be moved on the St Lawrence Canal system because the facilities available were inadequate for the handling of all grain destined for European markets. In the future a large proportion of this winter movement will be diverted to the Seaway with its increased handling potential, but some grain will probably still reach the Maritime ports. With storage facilities already existing at these ports it will probably be convenient to rail late grain either from the Prairies or the Georgian Bay ports in order both to alleviate pressure on existing storage facilities farther west and to exploit markets which may develop overseas during the winter months. The probable amount of the diversion from the Georgian Bay route is rather difficult to estimate. All the grain moving along this route was not export grain. Approximately a third was railed to local domestic processing centres. Grain ports developed on Georgian Bay chiefly because this general location is closer to the Lakehead than it is to Montreal, which makes it possible for a lake vessel to make shorter and more numerous journeys during the navigation season than between the Lakehead and Montreal. In the future any reduction in the winter movement of grain via Maritime ports will also mean a reduction in the amount handled by the Georgian Bay ports, but the latter ports will without doubt continue to handle grain for domestic consumption within parts of Ontario at least.

Estimates of the saving in transport costs on wheat, especially, have ranged all the way from a few cents up to 15 or 16 cents. In 1956 it was already cheaper to move a bushel of wheat from certain points in Alberta to the British Isles via the St Lawrence ports than via Pacific ports in spite of both a more expensive rail haul to the Lakehead than to Vancouver and two transhipment charges on the St Lawrence. It was 8 cents cheaper via the St Lawrence route, but this route was not equipped to handle the total amount of grain for export so that large quantities of wheat destined for Europe had to move via the Pacific ports, anyway. In the Seaway era it is likely that the differential of 8 cents will perhaps be doubled, even allowing for toll charges, so that if storage facilities are increased and the railways are equipped to handle an increased movement to the Lakehead, then there should be a considerable diversion from the Pacific ports to the Seaway.

There is another major question in regard to grain movement. To what extent will ocean-going vessels be responsible for the movement of grain on the Great Lakes–St Lawrence waterway? Hartley expresses the opinion that large volumes of grain can be expected to

The Future

move by all three types of vessels – lake carriers, ocean liners and
tramps. Some authorities have suggested that the bulk of grain for
export would be moved by lakers as far as Montreal or other lower
St Lawrence ports, to be there transhipped to ocean vessels. Because
of the capacity of these vessels and the relative ease with which they
move through the inland waterways, it has long been considered that
grain movement by lakers would be more economical than by ocean
vessels. Estimates of considerable savings in transport charges have
chiefly been made on the basis of the back-loading of iron ore or some
other bulk commodity. These claims for a significant back-loading
traffic appear to be greatly exaggerated. It is unlikely that the ore-
carrier fleets of the Middle Western steel companies will be available
for grain movement. In normal years the steel companies will want
to move as much ore as possible via the shorter and cheaper Seaway
route from Seven Islands during the short navigation season. Participation in grain movement would involve a journey from one or
other of the Lake Erie ore ports to the Lakehead or any other grain
ports which might develop on the Great Lakes, to load up with
grain and then undertake what would most likely be a longer return
journey to Seven Islands, unloading either at one of the present
transhipment ports on the lower St Lawrence or at Seven Islands.
Normal transhipment charges would undoubtedly be increased due
to the necessity of having to convert an ore carrier to a grain carrier,
and this extra charge, in addition to the cost of the extra distance
covered to load up with grain, might well nullify any economy which
would result from back-loading. This reduction or nullification of
savings and the critical extra day or two involved in journeying to a
grain port suggest that lake carriers might not hold the great advantage over ocean vessels so often claimed for them.

However, other factors favour the use of lakers over ocean vessels.
To fully exploit the relatively cheap form of transport provided by
lakers it will be necessary for any one laker in the grain trade to make
as many round trips as possible during the navigation season. Certain
forms of ocean vessels will be able to carry grain to lower St Lawrence ports or the equivalent distance at a lower rate than the large
lakers, but the total amount of grain moved in this manner will
probably not be large because the journey's end for the ocean vessel
will be a European port and the round trip, including the time spent

loading general cargo for the return journey, will take too long a period of time. Nevertheless, there is no reason why ocean vessels should not share in the grain movement to a much greater extent than has been suggested up to date.

The Seaway was primarily built for the iron ore and grain trade. To the Middle Western steel industry the Seaway was the logical alternative to the combined ocean and rail route via Atlantic ports, for the movement of Quebec-Labrador iron ore. In the first five years ore shipments are expected to average 10 million tons annually and before the end of the second five-year period the total should have increased to 20 million tons or more. With anywhere near normal economic conditions it appears at the present time that the annual shipment of ore may be greater in twenty years' time than present estimates suggest. For steel centres west of Pittsburgh the Seaway route will offer considerable savings over the longer ocean or lower St Lawrence and rail route.

Within the entire Great Lakes–St Lawrence system there are four significant movements of iron ore. The major movement is of course between United States Lake Superior ore ports and the ore ports on Lakes Michigan, Erie and Ontario. The tonnage shipped from Lake Superior ports has on occasion exceeded 100 million tons. Within the future this amount is not likely to vary a great deal; but eventually, with a decline in the output of the Mesabi mines particularly, this movement will decrease in significance. Movements from the Steep Rocks mines to the north of Lake Superior to United States ports and from Michipicoten, also north of Lake Superior, to Sault Ste Marie are not likely to be affected to any extent by the Seaway. The fourth significant movement is of course that of Quebec-Labrador ore. At times in the future iron ore may make up between 40 per cent and 50 per cent of traffic on the Seaway.

It is much more difficult to forecast the future movements of coal, coke and petroleum. They are all moved in considerable quantities at the present time, particularly coal, which moves outward from the Appalachian coalfields via Lake Erie ports to United States Lake Superior ports, Lake Ontario ports and those of the lower St Lawrence. The improvement of navigation facilities on the Great Lakes is not likely to influence the movement of coal, coke and petroleum between Great Lakes ports, but due to improvement of the Welland

and upper St Lawrence section of the Seaway more United States coal for Europe may follow this route. United States coal for Europe is presently shipped through the ports of Hampton Roads, Baltimore and Philadelphia. In 1956 a total of 41 million tons of bituminous coal was shipped abroad through these ports and indications are that this total will increase rapidly in the years ahead. The largest shipments of this export coal went to Germany (10 million tons), Italy (7·5 million tons), France (6·6 million tons), Netherlands (6·6 million tons), and the United Kingdom, Belgium and Austria. The same coal could move to the ports of Toledo and Sandusky at freight charges of between 32 and 59 cents less than to Atlantic coast ports. The distance from the Lake Erie ports' to, say, Hamburg is very little different than the distance from Baltimore to Hamburg. However, the time consumed in locks and canals will be greater than open ocean sailing, and whatever tolls are charged on the Seaway will offset to some extent the freight-rate advantage of the Great Lakes loading ports, but all things considered it seems that considerable quantities of United States coal for export might well be moving along the St Lawrence route by 1965. The market in the Middle West for the return load of general cargo should prove equally as good as the Atlantic coast market.

More coal and coke may also move through the Welland Canal to the steel mills at Hamilton, where furnace capacity is being increased, and possibly through the upper St Lawrence to new steel plants planned for sites on the banks of the lower St Lawrence. This coal would, however, compete with Maritime coal. At this stage it is difficult to say just how far United States and Maritime coal and coke can profitably be moved on the Seaway. If the downstream movement of United States coal and coke becomes a back-loading movement on ore carriers bound for Seven Islands to load up with Quebec-Labrador iron ore, then United States coal and coke will probably compete with Maritime coal and coke well down the St Lawrence, in spite of subsidised transportation of Maritime coal and coke. However, within the next five to ten years it is possible that the demand for coal in the Montreal area, at least, might decline because of competition from natural gas. From then on there should be an increased demand because of the industrial growth which will undoubtedly follow the completion of the Seaway. It is not unlikely that the demands of this industrial growth, together with the coal requirements of thermal power-plants which will be needed in ports of the upper St Lawrence to supplement St Lawrence hydro-power, may amount to several million tons of additional coal.

Only the estimates of the United States Department of Commerce show any considerable increase in the movement of petroleum on the Seaway. United States or Canadian oil will soon be reaching almost every major city in the Great Lakes–St Lawrence region by pipeline so that it seems most unlikely that there will be any significant increase in movement by tankers in the near future.

In recent years, with the completion of a pipeline from the Canadian west to southern Ontario, tanker transportation of the same oil from Duluth has been supplanted to an increasing extent. At one time it was thought that large quantities of Middle East crude might reach the Middle West via the Seaway; but as the tankers involved

TRAFFIC ON THE GREAT LAKES–ST LAWRENCE SYSTEM, 1953

Products	Sault Ste Marie	Welland	St Lawrence
UPBOUND			
Agricultural	11,861	19,200	7,890
Coal and Coke	8,701,539	24,178	22,780
Iron Ores and Others	224,887	132,976	171,902
Paper and Wood	—	824,756	831,544
Automobiles and Parts	—	1,101	1,479
Petroleum	621,548	814,224	984,420
Iron and Steel	38,671	136,890	147,245
Others	2,098,566	629,137	829,837
Total	11,697,072	2,582,462	2,997,097
DOWNBOUND			
Agricultural	13,307,528	5,589,758	4,360,359
Coal and Coke	5,000	5,949,459	1,563,716
Iron Ores and Others	98,432,704	2,999,674	4,700
Paper and Wood	482,840	178,970	4,383
Automobiles and Parts	—	2,008	2,715
Petroleum	3,342,632	1,524,581	275,072
Iron and Steel	568,397	101,013	12,288
Others	662,997	614,225	861,662
Total	116,802,098	16,959,688	7,084,895

The Future

in this trade are, in general, much too large for the Seaway, development in this direction is limited. Transhipment at a lower St Lawrence port would be possible, but it is doubtful whether the Seaway route would then have any advantages over Atlantic ports or Gulf ports and the Mississippi route. The upbound movement on the St Lawrence is at the present largely one of petroleum products from the Montreal refineries, using Venezuelan and Middle Eastern crude, which reaches the refineries largely via the Portland pipeline. Expansion of the Montreal refineries is limited by space and with increasing quantities of Canadian crude arriving in eastern Canada there would seem to be the likelihood of a diminishing market in southern Ontario.

In addition to the movement of bulk commodities either within the Great Lakes–St Lawrence region or between Great Lakes ports and overseas, there is the promise of a rapid development in the movement of general cargo. All estimates allow for a considerable increase in this movement. While initial volumes of such cargo are expected to be small relative to the bulk movements, estimates are hampered by a lack of long-term experience and may not reflect the ultimate market for this traffic. As mentioned in an earlier chapter, there is the possibility of both a considerable internal movement of general cargo, that is between the industrial districts adjoining the Great Lakes–St Lawrence system, as well as overseas trade. The former will increase as a natural outcome of improved navigation and port facilities, the increased availability of power and the industrial growth which is anticipated.

What measure of increase can be expected in the overseas trade in general cargo? The export and import trade with Europe and other overseas ports has been developing rapidly in volume since the end of the Second World War. An increased number of services are now provided and trade connections have developed. In fact all the preliminary work necessary for the expansion of a new trade route has been carried out. In the long run perhaps it is this trade, based on the savings to be obtained from direct shipment by water, which will provide the most conspicuous evidence of the Seaway's existence deep into Great Lakes territory. In 1957 there were 25 shipping lines and 133 vessels involved in Great Lakes-overseas trade, and most of these vessels were handling either all or some general cargo.

Several recent publications indicate the nature of the savings which can be expected in the transportation of general cargo via the Seaway rather than the Atlantic or Gulf route. A publication of the United States Maritime Administration contains a number of interesting rate comparisons which suggest the freight cost savings already available by shipping via the Great Lakes. For instance, corn syrup and glucose originating at Peoria, Illinois, can be shipped to Antwerp, by rail to Chicago and by water beyond, at a combined rate of $1.18 per hundredweight, as compared to combination rail-water rates from $1.36 to $1.51 via eastern seaboard ports. Canned goods in boxes from St Louis to Chicago by rail and by water beyond, again to Antwerp, is $1.71 per hundredweight opposed to rail-water rates via Atlantic ports of $1.83 to $1.86.

Machinery originating in Minneapolis can reach Antwerp via Milwaukee at a rate of $2.96, whereas the same shipment via east-coast ports would carry rates ranging from $3.49 to $3.55. These rates are existing rates. Lower operating costs to the ship-owners using the improved Seaway should be reflected in downward rate adjustments.

An official of the Willys-Overland Export Corporation of Toledo recently predicted a 500 per cent increase in his firm's export trade through the port of Toledo when the Seaway is available. He compared a cost of $5.50 for delivering a jeep to the pier in Toledo as against $53.62 for delivering the same jeep to an eastern seaboard pier. In 1957 *Seaway Soundings*, a publication of the port of Cleveland, made a cost comparison of a specific shipment, a 168,000-pound 'Moto-Crane' from Lorain, Ohio, through Cleveland to Manchester, England. The combined inland and ocean freight amounted to $13,808, whereas had it gone via an east-coast port it would have amounted to $14,865. Taking into account the proposed toll on general cargo, this saving would be reduced from $1,057 to $991.95.

An overseas cargo combination which has been suggested as most likely for the future is that of high-rate general cargo and certain low-rate bulk cargoes termed in the trade 'bottom' cargo. Grain is expected to be an important 'bottom' cargo.

General cargo movement will undoubtedly benefit a great deal from the Seaway, perhaps even more so than the bulk commodities. This is not to say that the amount of general cargo will increase proportionally more than the movement of bulk commodities, but savings in transportation costs will probably be much greater in the case of general cargo movement. General cargo will benefit particularly from the reduction in handling losses and costs due to considerable elimination of transhipment. This factor, in addition to the shorter and more direct route to Europe, as well as the economies resulting from the greater capacity of the vessels which will be able to use the Seaway, provide the low-cost transportation which will favour this route over the Atlantic and Gulf ports route for the movement of general cargo especially.

SHIPPING AND THE SEAWAY

To what extent will the proposed 27-foot channel and the dimensions of the future locks meet the anticipated demand? The answer to this question depends on a number of factors. Firstly, is the provision of 27-foot navigation going to give rise to a 'lakeway' between the upper Great Lakes and the lower St Lawrence as suggested in Chapter 3, or will a 'seaway' develop, one open to the majority of the ocean-going vessels of the world. In other words, will the vessels on the St Lawrence and the Great Lakes in the future be predominantly of the 'upper laker' class, long, slim, relatively shallow type vessels, specially built for efficient transportation of bulk commodities, or will they be ocean-going vessels, typical freighters and tramps which have come in from the Atlantic and the other oceans of the world? The answer to this question very definitely is that lakers will predominate because of the very large quantities of bulk commodities, especially iron ore and grain, which have to be moved during the restricted navigation season. The present upper-lake fleet, with a range in capacity from 4,600 to 22,600 short tons, will probably be inadequate to handle the estimated potential traffic. Specialised ships are already being built to supplement the present lake fleet and to replace the present fleet as it becomes depreciated. Some of these special vessels will weigh up to 25,000 tons. Some specialised dual-service ships of up to 20,000 tons are also being constructed. These ships will travel the Seaway in summer and the oceans in winter. It is difficult to say at present just what prospects there are for such 'dual service' ships.

And what of ocean-going vessels? An opinion expressed earlier is here repeated. The opening of the Seaway will open the upper St

The St Lawrence Seaway

Lawrence and the Great Lakes to a much higher proportion of the world's shipping than at present. There are certainly sufficient ships available at the present time to handle all the general cargo that is likely to be available for Seaway shipping and there is a considerable number of ships under construction in Europe especially for the Seaway trade. A step-up in the rate of industrial expansion in the Great Lakes–St Lawrence region will undoubtedly result from the completion of the Seaway and Power projects. Much of the expansion is likely to take place in areas adjacent to the shores of the Great Lakes or the banks of the St Lawrence. There is very little likelihood that any combination of rail and/or truck and ocean transportation will be able to compete with straight Seaway and ocean transportation in the trade between this expanding industrial region and overseas markets, especially Europe. If there is profitable shipping to be done, ships will be there.

Obviously there are several factors which might well reduce the appeal of the Seaway to shipowners, both North American and overseas. Fears have been expressed for some time that the Seaway has been built to entirely inadequate capacity, not only from the point of view of depth, but also width of channels, size of locks and the lack of double locks throughout the St Lawrence and on a part of the Welland. The slowness of the inland passage has probably been greatly exaggerated. Passage in any canal system is slower than on the ocean routeways. Many critics have taken the estimates of potential traffic and have calculated that the Seaway could not possibly handle the amount of shipping necessary without considerable delays in lockages. It would appear most likely that if Seaway traffic increases as anticipated, then both the United States and Canada will further improve facilities. Provision has been made for double locks throughout the Seaway whenever the traffic demands it. Most experts agree that the Welland Canal will eventually constitute a bottleneck if potential traffic is realised, but here some double locks already exist, and additional double locks could be constructed readily. The width of the Seaway channel will probably restrict speed to about 12 m.p.h., which in the case of modern lakers and ocean vessels is anywhere from 1 to 4 or 5 m.p.h. below maximum speed. However, maximum speed will be possible on the Great Lakes and the lower St Lawrence.

The Future

Critics also point to the ice and fog hazards on the inland water-way, but these are probably no greater than those encountered by all shipping on the North Atlantic. The navigation season on the St Lawrence is ordinarily eight months long, but it does vary by a week or two from year to year. For late shipping there is always the danger of an early freeze-up. The earliest and most severe freeze-up in modern shipping history came in the final year of the old canal system, when late shipping had to fight its way through thick ice to Montreal harbour, only to become ice-bound there until mid-January of 1959. The opening of the Seaway will not offset the repetition of such an occurrence, but the very fact that these ships did finally escape from the St Lawrence as the result of successful work by icebreakers suggests that in the future a team of icebreakers might well extend the navigation season at both ends. An 'all-year' Seaway is even being spoken of at the present time. Canadian government sources have reported that with an increase in the number and the efficiency of icebreakers, the use of aerial ice surveys, and the improvement of aids to navigation, winter navigation, at least on the lower St Lawrence, is possible.

Fears have also recently been expressed that pilotage charges on the Seaway might become prohibitive. Only the future will tell.

TOLLS

A final factor of concern to all who plan to use the Seaway in the future is the tolls structure. Up to date the final tolls structure for the Seaway has not been announced, but the Canadian and United States Tolls Committees have announced the following proposals: For through traffic on the St Lawrence Canals a toll charge of 4 cents per ton on a vessel's gross registered tonnage plus 40 cents per ton on bulk cargo and 90 cents per ton on general cargo; for through traffic on the Welland Canal, 2 cents per gross registered ton plus 2 cents per ton of bulk cargo and 5 cents per ton of package freight. On the assumption that gross registered tonnage and cargo carried are equal for any particular vessel, the total charge for both the St Lawrence and Welland Canals would amount to 48 cents per ton of bulk cargo and $1.01 per ton of package freight. The Tolls Committee further proposes that for movement between two Canadian or two United States points vessels of, on the one hand, Canadian registry and, on the other, United States registry pay only the same toll per ton of general cargo as per ton of bulk cargo.

The principal toll would be based upon the cargo actually carried. The method recommended is based primarily on the tonnage carried, or the use being made of the Seaway in terms of commodities transported. With the principal toll based upon the cargo carried, vessels which are travelling the Seaway partially laden are not penalised.

GREAT LAKES–ST LAWRENCE OVERSEAS TRAFFIC

These firms already are operating directly between the
Great Lakes and foreign ports

Service	Areas Served
Ahlmann Transcaribbean Line	Caribbean
Anchor Line Ltd.	U.K.
Bristol City Line	U.K.
Canadian Pacific Steamships	U.K.
Cunard Steam-Ship Company	U.K.
Donaldson Line	U.K.
Ellerman Great Lakes Line	Mediterranean
Fabre Line	Mediterranean
Finlake Line	U.K., Baltic
Fjell Line	Scandinavia
Fjell-Oranje Lines	U.K., West Europe
French Line	West Europe
Furness Great Lakes Line	U.K.
Great Lakes Joint Service	West Europe
Head Line	U.K.
Liverpool Liners Limited	U.K.
Manchester Liners Limited	U.K.
Montship–Capo Great Lakes Service	Mediterranean, N.W. Africa
Niagara Line	Mediterranean
Poseidon Lines	North Sea
Saguenay Shipping Limited	Caribbean
Swedish American Line	West Europe, Scandinavia
Swedish Chicago Line	Baltic–Scandinavia
Wallenius Line	North Sea, Scandinavia
Zim Israel American Lines	Mediterranean

The Future

GREAT LAKES OVERSEAS SCHEDULED SERVICES
(based on traffic passing through the Welland Ship Canal)

| | | | | NUMBER | PERIOD OF | |
| | NUMBER OF VESSELS OPERATING | | | OF TRIPS | OPERATION | |
Year	Total	Scheduled	Non-Scheduled	All vessels	First Inbound	Last Outbound
1946	12	12	0	21	May 2	Nov. 24
1947	15	15	0	37	April 29	Nov. 29
1948	25	23	2	58	April 29	Nov. 28
1949	28	23	5	73	April 26	Nov. 16
1950	44	29	15	95	April 25	Nov. 14
1951	40	33	7	100	April 25	Nov. 27
1952	60	43	17	145	April 23	Dec. 1
1953	119	66	53	268	April 17	Dec. 2
1954	100	73	27	267	April 22	Dec. 4
1955	119	87	32	329	April 22	Dec. 3
1956	125	97	28	334	April 21	Dec. 2
1957	133	96	37	351	April 20	Dec. 4

Furthermore, it relieves a vessel engaged in carrying a single bulk commodity one way of the high cost of returning in ballast. This is an inducement for ships to enter the Great Lakes partially laden. Many ocean-going vessels cannot transit the Seaway completely laden, so that such vessels would pay according to what they are actually earning instead of according to their potential earning capacity.

It is of interest to note that the tolls structure now under consideration by the Seaway entities is in contrast to that used by the Panama and Suez Canals. For laden vessels using the Panama Canal the rate is 90 cents per net vessel ton of 100 cubic feet of actual earning capacity or usable space. For vessels in ballast the rate is 72 cents per net vessel ton. For the Suez Canal the rate for laden ships is equivalent to $97\frac{1}{2}$ cents per net registered ton and $44\frac{1}{2}$ cents per net vessel ton for ships in ballast. By way of comparison, one could take a general cargo ship of 8,000 tons. With 8,000 tons of cargo, 50 per cent general cargo and 50 per cent bulk, the charge for a one-way passage between Montreal and Lake Erie on the Seaway would average 77.44 cents per ton. For the Panama Canal the average would be 87 cents per ton, and for the Suez Canal it would be 96 cents per ton.

Although the proposed tolls structure has its critics, the general consensus of opinion is that tolls will not jeopardize the future of the Seaway, though there is one threat to the future. President Eisenhower recently disclosed that the United States portion of the Seaway would soon come under the jurisdiction of the U.S. Department of Commerce. United States Seaway supporters, fearing the tampering with tolls, have fought against the change, lest United States railroads should be able thereby to exert influence to get higher tolls and thus to throw a major roadblock in the way of Seaway shipping.

THE FUTURE OF GREAT LAKES AND ST LAWRENCE PORTS

At the present time practically every port on the Great Lakes and the St Lawrence is expecting to benefit from the completion of the Seaway. If the Great Lakes–St Lawrence region undergoes rapid industrial expansion as a result of the Seaway, then almost every port can expect to benefit somewhat. Obviously some will gain a great deal more than others. Expansion will not depend alone upon geographic location, but also upon the extent to which ports improve their facilities and their approach channels so that lakers and overseas vessels will be attracted. As early as April 1955 the Canadian National Harbours Board reported that thirteen ports between Portneuf on the lower St Lawrence and Sarnia on Lake Huron had requested improvements. Until such time as definite predictions can be made about the freight potentials of lake harbours, and actual patterns of trade have been established, assistance will be concentrated on providing deep-water facilities at Toronto, Hamilton, Fort William and Port Arthur. Some assistance will be extended to other ports, but it is unlikely that many of these will ever be provided with deep-water facilities.

In the United States Chicago, Gary, Milwaukee, Detroit, Duluth, Toledo, Cleveland, Buffalo, Oswego and Ogdensburg have all launched major improvement programmes. Of course, several of these ports are already equipped to handle deep-draught ore and grain-carriers, so that channel deepening is not a major objective. Most of the money being spent is going into extra berthage space,

The Future

grain elevators and cargo terminals. Chicago and Milwaukee would appear to have excellent prospects of capturing the bulk of the grain trade, and both ports should also attract considerable general overseas trade. Most of the major ore ports on Lake Erie will benefit from the additional handling of Canadian ore. Buffalo, Oswego and Ogdensburg are all expecting to benefit from participation in the overseas trade. Buffalo will undoubtedly lose some of the grain trade, but will probably gain a considerable share of the overseas trade, being the first major United States port on the Seaway.

Though Montreal at one time feared the completion of the Seaway, the city is now ready to exploit what has become appreciated as a most advantageous position. It has already been suggested that rather than the Seaway providing a route to the Great Lakes for ocean shipping there will be provided a connection between the upper Great Lakes and the lower St Lawrence, especially Montreal. It is

COMMERCE HANDLED BY MAJOR UNITED STATES AND CANADIAN CANALS AND PORTS
1951

	Tons (millions)
Duluth-Superior	73
St Mary's Falls Canal	120
Detroit River	132
Toledo	31
Welland Canal	18
Ogdensburg to Montreal, 14-foot Canal	10
New York Harbour	152
Delaware River, below Trenton	73
Baltimore	43
Ohio River	57
Mississippi River, Minneapolis to the Passes	73
Gulf Intracoastal Waterway, 12-foot Depth	36
Sabine-Neches Waterway	54
Houston Ship Channel	44
New Orleans	38
San Francisco Bay Area	34
Montreal	15

possible that Montreal will expand rapidly as a transhipment point for grain. Montreal's function as a transhipment point for general cargo for the interior will probably decline, but the general economic growth of the city should be stimulated tremendously by the completion of the Seaway.

Of the other Canadian ports, perhaps Toronto and Hamilton stand the best chance of benefiting from the Seaway. Toronto claims that it will become the leading port of the Great Lakes for overseas shipping and that ships laden with general cargo for western Canada will prefer to unload at Toronto rather than undertake the long, slow journey to the Lakehead. Hamilton will gain from the boost given to the steel industry by the arrival of Quebec-Labrador ore and perhaps cheaper coal. Hamilton also expects to become a major transhipment point.

Every port has its claims, but only time will tell. Some are several steps ahead already because of the important trade connections which have been established, some are being favoured by the provision of deep-water navigation and some have geographic advantages which cannot be denied.

Index

153

Index

Index

155

Index

Index